Kaokoveld
The last wilderness

Kaokoveld
The last wilderness

Anthony Hall~Martin,
Clive Walker and
J du P Bothma

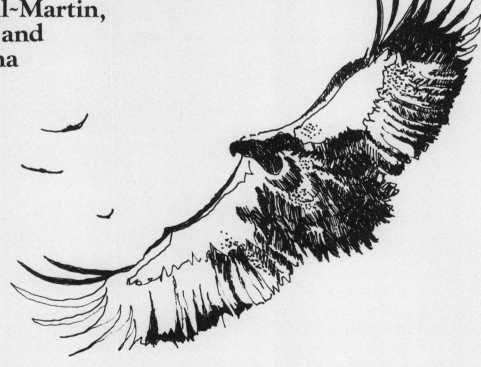

SOUTHERN
BOOK PUBLISHERS

*All photographs are by the authors, except for eight by
Professor F.C. Eloff. These are the Marienfluss
(p. 95), tree in rain (p. 101), giraffes, ostriches and gemsbok
(pp. 116-7), scorpion, snake and lizard in sand (p. 119).*

The map on p. 2 is adapted from P.J. Viljoen, *South African
Journal of Zoology* 1987: 22 (4). The map on p. 54
is adapted from J.S. Malan, *Cimbebasia* 1973: Ser. B. 2 (3).

ISBN 1 86812 140 2

First edition, first impression 1988
First edition, second impression 1989

Published by
Southern Book Publishers (Pty) Ltd
P O Box 548, Bergvlei 2012
Johannesburg

Set in 11 on 13 pt Palatino
by Book Productions, Pretoria
Printed and bound by CTP Book Printers, Cape

BK0618

This book is dedicated to

Professor Fritz Eloff, and to the memory of Bernabe de la Bat and
Ina Britz

Foreword

by David Shepherd, O.B.E.

There are still some wild and wonderful places that have more or less escaped the destructive hand of man and I have been lucky to have visited a few of them. One is the Kaokoveld. Just to breathe the air and tread ground that is truly remote is a totally fulfilling experience; to go in the company of men whose hearts are in the land and its creatures only adds emphasis to the magic. Such men are Clive Walker, Koos Bothma and Anthony Hall-Martin.

This beautiful world is the only one that we have and we cannot make it any bigger. We should remind ourselves, therefore, that to arrogantly assume that we can go on for ever using up its finite resources and destroying the habitat is not only supremely stupid, but dangerous. We do not own this earth to do with it what we please; we share it with all living creatures — on whom we depend, as they do on us — and to assume otherwise will ultimately lead, I believe, to our own self-destruction.

When I was in the Kaokoveld, I came face to face with one of those very special and unique creatures, the desert elephant. I have seen countless elephants on so many occasions in Africa, but this was something very special indeed. I felt I was intruding on his privacy, because this was his territory and not mine. He was totally at peace. He knew we were there, but he was trusting us to leave him alone. I was privileged to be in the company of this great, noble but desperately threatened animal.

We hold this world in trust for future generations, and the future is in their hands. Conservation does not just mean raising money. Awareness through education is even more important. If young people know just how fragile this world is and that there are wide open, clean places like the Kaokoveld, then they will realise just how precious these places are.

David Shepherd

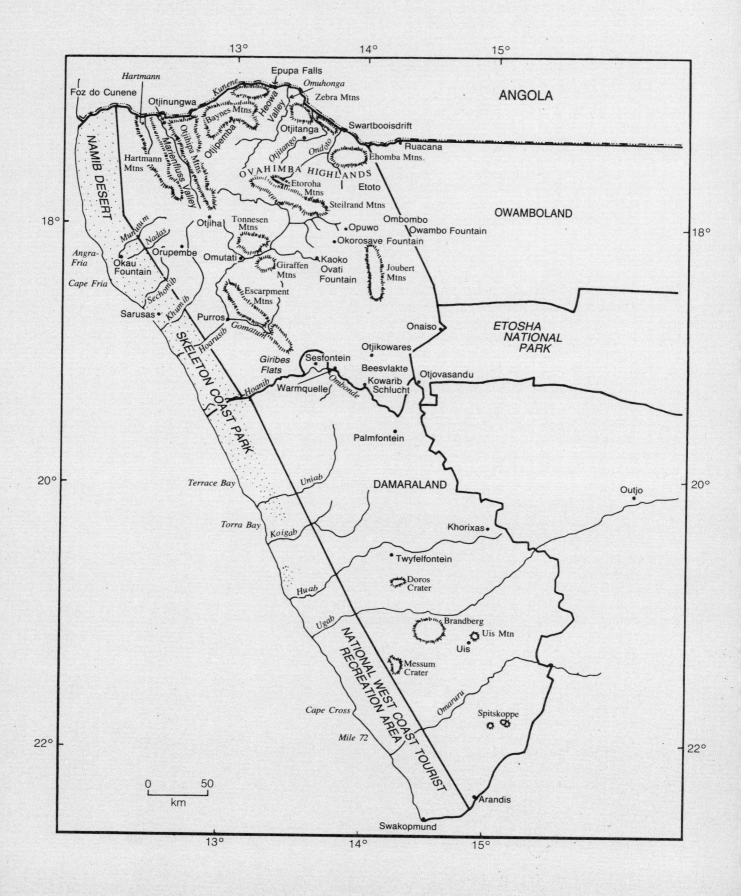

Introduction

Where, or what, is the Kaokoveld? Why have we used the title 'The Last Wilderness' to describe this area? Since the last century *Kaokoveld* has been used to describe the generally arid northwestern corner of South West Africa/Namibia. It encompasses the modern territories of Kaokoland and Damaraland, part of the mosaic of ethnically based homelands making up the country which is to become Namibia. The term was used by Captain G.C. Shortridge in his monumental work on the mammals of South West Africa, published in 1934, and by many writers after him, to describe that area stretching from the Ugab River to the Kunene, and from the coast inland to around the present-day eastern boundary of Kaokoland and the boundaries where Damaraland abuts on the magisterial districts of Outjo, Otjiwarongo, Omaruru and Karibib. Though we have accepted the political boundaries of the two territories of Kaokoland and Damaraland as defining the formal area of our attention, it is in reality the Kaokoveld of Shortridge which concerns us.

We have called it the last wilderness because among our circle of friends and colleagues are the last men who knew this area as it still was in the late 1960s. Then it was a remote part of primeval Africa, with undeveloped African landscapes, abundant wildlife and dignified traditional people. Now modernity, with its blessings and curses, has changed that old order. A new situation fraught with promise and problems has arisen. We would not deny the people of the Kaokoveld their move into the modern world with its promise of education, political rights, modern conveniences and facilities. But we lament the loss of an ecologically based system of life in which man and wildlife lived compatibly and neither destroyed the other. The future will be different, because the wilderness has almost all gone.

In 1974, Professor Fritz Eloff, then head of the Department of Zoology at the University of Pretoria, was commissioned by the South African government to undertake an ecological survey of Kaokoland and Damaraland. He asked his university colleagues Professor Jacobus du P. Bothma of the Eugène Marais Chair of Wildlife Management, Professor Guillaume Theron of the Botany Department and Professor Willem van Riet to assist. Several expeditions to the Kaokoveld were undertaken and reports were submitted in 1977.

In 1978 Professor Eloff invited Clive Walker, then Director of the Endangered Wildlife Trust, to visit the Kaokoveld with him. Clive found the area fascinating. But what interested him most was the parlous state of the desert elephants and black rhino, which to all appearances were being hunted to extinction, both legally and illegally, with little control exercised by the authorities in Pretoria responsible for the area. Clive and his colleagues on the Trust, in particular Peter Joffe, recognised that for these unique animals the hour was late. Every visit of the Pretoria University team produced a new record of carcasses and bleached bones. Action had to be taken to stop the slaughter. Clive then mobilised the resources of the Endangered Wildlife Trust and created an unprecedented awareness of the situation in the local and overseas media. Clive's actions also played an inspirational role in the formation of the Namibia Wildlife Trust (N.W.T.) whose first priority was the conservation of the elephants and black rhino of Damaraland.

Garth Owen-Smith and Karl Peter Erb were appointed by the N.W.T. to start an active conservation and education campaign in the area. Operations were centered on Wêreldsend, the base camp of Colin and Ina Britz, who played a major role in the conservation programmes which followed. An auxiliary game guard force which worked under the local tribal headmen on anti-poaching operations was organised. In 1980 the Directorate of Nature Conservation and Tourism (D.N.C.) appointed an officer, Chris Eyre, stationed at Khorixas. In time the entire project was handed over to the Directorate and more appointments followed at Sesfontein and at Opuwo, but the Endangered Wildlife Trust continues to fund the auxiliary game guard system. From time to time other organisations have also contributed to the programmes which have been supported by the Damaraland Representative Council.

Though the D.N.C. now handles law enforcement in the area, the role of outside fundraisers, channelling their efforts through the D.N.C., continues to be important. This book has been written for the Rhino and Elephant Foundation as part of a joint effort with David Shepherd and the Southern African Nature Foundation to raise funds for conservation projects in the Kaokoveld. It has been published to provide an introduction to a wilderness the like of which exists nowhere else on earth.

Acknowledgements

While this book is based on personal observations and experience it freely incorporates the observations of others gleaned from the literature, discussions and correspondence. As it would have been burdensome to give chapter and verse for each source or observation, we hereby gratefully acknowledge the debt owed the many naturalists, nature conservation officers and scientists whose work has added to the value of this book.

We have appended a bibliography of the most important published sources of our information. We would, however, like to mention in particular the work of P. J. 'Slang' Viljoen and Garth Owen-Smith, who have contributed more than most to our knowledge of the wildlife and ecology of Kaokoland and Damaraland. They have not only amassed a formidable amount of information on the Kaokoveld, but have also made it available to such as ourselves who have tried to put their knowledge to work in helping to conserve this great wilderness.

We have been fortunate, over a period of several years, to have been able to visit the Kaokoveld and to meet the people working there. We have enjoyed hospitality, help, companionship and valuable contributions towards the ideal of conserving this most unusual area. We would like to thank all who have helped, but in particular Professors Fritz Eloff, Guillaume Theron and Willem van Riet, Garth Owen-Smith, Slang Viljoen, Colin and the late Ina Britz and Blythe Loutit.

Among the other colleagues, companions and friends whom we would like to thank for their help are Peter Hitchins, Peter Joffe, Ernst Taeuber, Petra Mengel, Jane Zimmerman, Ingrid Schroeder, Chloe Rolfes, Iain Douglas-Hamilton and Oria Douglas-Hamilton, Wouter van Hoven, Heather Wildi and Herta Kolberg.

We are grateful to the many officers of the Directorate of Nature Conservation and Recreation Resorts of South West Africa/Namibia, such as Chris Eyre, Rudi Loutit, Marcellus Loots, Karl Peter Erb, Duncan Gilchrist, Steven Braine and Mike Griffin, who have assisted the conservation effort in the Kaokoveld. In particular we would like to thank the Director, Mr Polla Swart, and Dr Peet van der Walt for their understanding of our efforts to assist them in their vital conservation task and for their support for the publication of this book.

We are pleased to acknowledge the conservation bodies who have also played a role in supporting projects in the Kaokoveld over the years. We thank the Southern African Nature Foundation, Endangered Wildlife Trust, Namibia Wildlife Trust, People's Trust for Endangered Species,

SAVE (Foundation to Save African Endangered Wildlife), the Wildlife
Society of South West Africa (Save the Rhino Fund), and the Rhino and
Elephant Foundation. We also acknowledge the support of Mr S.
Tjongerero and the late Mr S. Gobs of the Damaraland Representative
Council.

Our warmest appreciation goes to Conita Walker, Babsie Bothma and
Catherina Hall-Martin for their support in many ways for this project. In
particular we thank Catherina Hall-Martin for her dedicated typing of the
manuscript.

We owe a special word of thanks to Sally Antrobus and Basil van
Rooyen of Southern Book Publishers for their support of this project.

Contents

Landscapes

The Kaokoveld encompasses a range of biomes or landscapes all neatly arranged parallel to one another. On the west is the forbidding Skeleton Coast — a region of rocks, fog, shipwrecks and desolation, washed by the waters of the Benguela current, which brings Antarctic cold to desert heat. Parallel to the beach lies the northern extension of the Namib desert — the oldest and most fascinating desert in the world. Fascinating because of the uniqueness and diversity of plant and animal life which it supports — from the *Welwitschia mirabilis*, a plant that has been on earth almost since time began, to the dancing white lady *Orchestrella longipes*, a strange spider of the dunes.

The desert dunes form a narrow band along the coast, seldom reaching further than 20 km inland except in the far north, where the sand extends 60 km from the coast. The sand desert is replaced eastwards by a zone of gravel plains, the inner or pro-Namib.

Further inland the escarpment mountains rise from the plains. The escarpment runs from Angola through the Kaokoveld and far to the south, where it becomes the great escarpment of South Africa. It is a broad chain of mountain ranges sometimes broken and cut by river valleys, deep gorges and chasms, sometimes a solid rock wall. To the east of the escarpment mountains lies the central drainage basin, itself an extension of the rugged and broken escarpment, and a transition to the next great region, the highlands. This high country extends as the interior plateau far to the east — beyond Etosha, beyond Bushmanland into Botswana, and eventually to the great interior plateau, the highveld of the Transvaal.

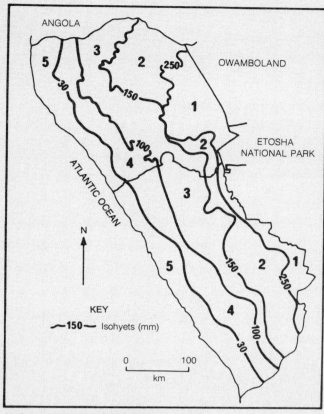

Isohyets and Bioclimatic Regions

The bioclimatic and physiographic regions of the Kaokoveld can be differently defined and to different levels of detail. For an introduction to the area, however, only five basic bioclimatic regions, subdivided into several physiographic types, need to be distinguished. These regions are defined by features of landscape type, which is a product of geological formation, soils, vegetation, rainfall pattern and temperature regime. However, the principal determinant of the bioclimatic regions, for our purposes, is moisture availability as measured by rainfall.

The plant communities of the Kaokoveld range from woodlands and savanna in the east on deep sandy soils with high rainfall, through shrublands where woody plants are sparse, to grassy plains with succulents and dwarf shrubs. Where rainfall is less than about 100 mm the vegetation consists of annual grasslands where bare rock desert and gravel plains one year can be waving fields of grass the next.

In the Namib the plants are scattered and adapted to survival in areas where it seldom rains. The most arid vegetation communities are those which are reduced to lichens on bare rock. The riverbeds, by virtue of the water under the sand, always support far more luxuriant vegetation than the plains on either side, from dense reedbeds to shady acacia forest.

The type of vegetation which can be expected is influenced by a number of environmental factors. The most fundamental determinant in the Kaokoveld is moisture. This can be derived from rain, subterranean flow, or condensed fog. Soil type and topography also play a role, but a lesser one. Topography is important in so far as it affects the distribution of rainfall and runoff or drainage. The physical nature of soils, which determines the availability of water, is probably of more consequence in determining the type of vegetation than is the chemical nature of the soil. Frost and fire can also play a role in determining whether a particular species occurs, or in influencing its growth form.

The only detailed study of the vegetation of Kaokoland is that carried out by Slang Viljoen and written up in 1977. Before him, Garth Owen-Smith had described the vegetation in a general way. R. I. de Sousa Correia had also reported on the vegetation of the northwestern part of Namibia. The vegetation of Damaraland has hardly been looked at by professional botanists other than Professor Guillaume Theron of the University of Pretoria. All of the above workers followed in the footsteps of W. Giess of the Windhoek Herbarium, who is the pioneer botanist of Namibia. For our purposes a brief botanical description of the Kaokoveld has been drawn from the material of the abovementioned workers.

Any attempt at describing the vegetation of an area close to 100 000 km², if not based on detailed study, must depend upon the use of certain indicator plants. Their presence, or absence, from a particular area is taken to indicate some prevailing environmental con-

2

dition which imposes a degree of uniformity upon an area. This is the most basic principle of vegetation classification, and is here used in a most elementary way.

Some examples of this approach are the distribution of mopane, *Colophospermum mopane*, and purple-pod terminalia or sterkbos, *Terminalia prunioides*. Both species are generally more typical of higher rainfall areas on the east of the subcontinent. Yet both are widespread in the Kaokoveld. The distribution of mopane ends at the edge of the inner Namib, except for its occurrence along river courses. Sterkbos does not occur as far to the west and only reaches the escarpment mountains. Tambotie, *Spirostachys africana*, occurs on the eastern plateau and westwards only along watercourses in the highlands and central drainage areas. *Terminalia sericea* indicates sandy soils, while the white syringa, *Kirkia acuminata*, is confined to rocky outcrops. The distribution of the various *Commiphora* species also tells a tale. At least four species only occur west of the 150 mm rainfall isohyet. They are *C. wildii*, the Swakopmund commiphora *(C. oblanceolata)*, *C. giessii* and *C. virgata*. Another suite of species, such as *C. mollis*, which is widespread in higher rainfall areas to the east of the subcontinent, and *C. angolensis*, are only found east of the 200 mm rainfall isohyet. *C. anacardifolia* is normally only found on rock outcrops on the edge of the Namib and *Adenolobus garipensis* also does not occur east of the desert margin.

Among the grasses, the perennial species are indicative of more mesic conditions than annuals (though this can be influenced by overgrazing wiping out perennials). Thus *Cenchrus ciliaris*, *Stipagrostis uniplumis* and *Aristida stipitata* only occur to the east while *Kaokochloa nigrirostris* and *Stipagrostis namaquensis* are typical of desert plains, and *S. hirtigluma* occurs widely in many vegetation types.

Plant communities can be described at different levels of detail. Thus, Viljoen recognised fourteen major vegetation types subdivided into numerous sub-types in Kaokoland alone. For our purposes, only seven vegetation zones, with some local variations, will be described.

The coastal desert and Skeleton Coast are barren, bleak and desolate, but with an almost overpowering grandeur and beauty. Much of the desert area within the Skeleton Coast Park is bare gravel plains where mirages abound and where plants are scarce — until it rains. From Terrace Bay southwards, salt pans, some of them fairly extensive, are a feature of the coastal region. The largest of these is the White Lady Salt Pan, which starts at Cape Cross and extends as far south as Mile 72, a distance of 16 km.

A continuous sand sheet commences at Torra Bay and stretches north to the Kunene. At the Hoarusib River, the dunes advance on a broad front from the south but are stopped by the river, which flows frequently enough to scour the sand out of its course. Immediately north of the Hoarusib, the dunefield is scarcely 5 km wide from east to west. From Sarusas to Angra Fria there are extensive salt pans and gravel flats which break up the sand sheet. North of Angra Fria the dunes once again cover the land and in the far north stretch from the coast to the western slopes of the Hartmann Mountains, a distance of 60 km. This area of unconsolidated sand dunes forms a sand sea, reminiscent of the region south of the Kuiseb River in the central Namib.

The sand dunes end at the Kunene, and on the north bank there is bare rock and gravel with only a narrow spit of sand at the mouth of the river at Foz do Cunene. The sand sheet widens rapidly into the Iona area and then gradually tails off, getting narrower towards Mossamedes.

The Skeleton Coast Park lies between the Ugab River in the south and the Kunene in the north. Its eastern boundary is a line on the map, 30–40 km from the coast. South of this the coastal area west of the Damaraland boundary forms the National West Coast Tourist Recreation Area, which stretches as far south as Swakopmund. Its main attraction is the rich fishing to be had along the fogbound coast, and for a growing clientele the beauty and isolation of one of the last great untouched areas on earth.

The coastal desert is devoid of vegetation over large areas, but particular localities nevertheless support a variety of plants — all adapted to the arid conditions — and about 70–80 species of higher plants are known to occur. The species composition of the northern Namib flora, while closely related to the flora of the central and southern Namib, is sufficiently different for it to have been recognised by Giess as a separate vegetation type. This decision is supported by the presence of at least six species of plants which are endemic to the northern Namib. They are *Merremia multisecta, Indigofera cunenensis, Petalidium angustitubum, Barleria solitaria, Ectadium virgatum* var. *rotundifolium* and the grass *Stipagrostis ramulosa.*

The desert is bounded inland by the 30 mm rainfall isohyet, where the desert vegetation is replaced by the more conspicuous grasses of the inner Namib gravel and sand plains.

The substrate for plant life in the coastal desert is unconsolidated sand, coarse gravel flats, sandy gravel plains or gravel plains with scattered rocks or rock outcrops. This material has undergone minimal soil-forming processes and contains very little organic matter for plant nutrition. The plants that grow here — other than those species which are limited to the river courses — are usually small, spreading shrubs seldom more than 40 cm in height.

Rain seldom falls in the coastal Namib desert (long-term mean annual rainfall at Mowe Bay is 13,3 mm) and the main source of moisture for plants as well as animals is the almost nightly sea fog which gently drifts over the dunes and plains, leaving droplets of condensation on the plants and sand. The fog usually reaches 40–50 km inland and some-

times as far as the escarpment mountains. The lower reaches of the rivers that cut through the desert are a major source of water. Though the water is deep under the sand it is available to plants with extensive root systems.

Several specialised plants grow along the coast and form small, low sand hummocks. Plants such as the dollar bush (*Zygophyllum stapfi*), the low-growing coastal ganna (*Salsola aphylla*) and narra (*Acanthosicyos horrida*) have an extensive root system under the sand which helps to stabilise the dune hummocks. These plants also provide a major source of food for insects and other animals of the desert. Among the many adaptations for survival shown by these plants are thick fleshy leaves covered by a wax cuticle to prevent water loss.

A few annual grasses are found in the dunes and these grow quickly after rain has fallen, set seed and then disappear. One of these is *Brachiaria psammophila*, whose specific name indicates a link to sand. *Eragrostis cyperoides* is found in the dunes from the Hoanib River northwards. The river courses are sometimes marked by dense thickets of tamarisk, *Tamarix usneoides*, but trees are absent. A prominent dune plant, after rain, is *Merremia multisecta*, which occurs from the Ugab northwards. It belongs to the same family as the morning glory and produces either creamy white flowers or white flowers with a dark purple centre.

At places along the coast the rivers end in pools of brackish water among the dunes. The delta of the Uniab is one such place and it is particularly well known for its pools of seepage water fringed by reeds (*Phragmites australis*) and several species of sedges such as *Juncellus laevigatus*, which forms dense mats, *Cyperus marginatus, Scirpus dioicus* and *S. littoralis*. These pools attract large numbers of birds — mainly Palaearctic waders of various species.

The vegetation of the gravel flats, especially to the south of the Uniab where there are no extensive sand dune areas, is dominated by *Hermannia gariepina*, which is a shrubby plant, and *Ectadium virgatum* var. *rotundifolium*, which was first described from the Torra Bay area. These plants are found widely scattered over large areas, together with a few other species such as the legumes *Indigofera cunenensis* (Cape Frio area) and *Crotalaria leubnitziana*. On the gravel and stony flats close to the coast lichen fields are very prominent. This is especially so near Sarusas, the Sechomib River and in the south. The lichens, a complex symbiosis of an algae and fungus, show up in bright colours in the early morning after fog. These colours range from yellow to grey-green and dark green, bluish, orange, red and white. Colour is also added to the gravel plains by succulent plants such as *Sesuvium sesuvioides*, which grows in low, spreading mats with dark green leaves and bright purple flowers.

The gravel flats along the coast are also the habitat of some very hardy grasses like *Stipagrostis ramulosa*, which forms a small low tussock in the lee of which miniature sand dunes a few centimetres high are formed. This grass was first collected in 1963 in the Uniab River and named by Dr Bernard de Winter, who is the present director of the Botanical Research Institute in Pretoria. This grass is scarce to the south of the Uniab but it becomes more abundant to the north. *Stipagrostis hermannii* is another of the ephemeral desert grasses.

The isolated rocky outcrops and hills of the northern Namib are not as large, nor do they support as diverse a flora as the inselbergs of the central Namib. Plants usually occur in protected sites among the rocks. Grasses are rare, but some species like *Asthenatherum glaucum* are found in sandy hollows between rocks. Most of the rock outcrop plants are dwarf shrubs like *Barleria solitaria* and *Othonna lasiocarpa*. Stone flowers are represented by *Lithops ruschiorum*, which has pinkish fleshy leaves that blend with the pink-tinged gravel among which it grows and which produces a single bright yellow flower.

Sadly, even a remote wilderness area like the Namib has already been invaded by exotic weeds. In most cases the seeds have been carried into the desert by floodwaters which originated on the eastern highlands. Among the exotics are *Datura innoxia*, the castor oil (*Ricinus communis*) and *Nicotiana glauca*, all of which are found from the Omaruru River northwards.

Adjoining the desert is the inner Namib or pro-Namib zone, where rainfall varies from 30 to 100 mm. The landscape is essentially flat, wide, semi-desert plains with scattered inselbergs separated by rugged, weathered chains of hills. The eastern boundary is formed by the escarpment mountains.

The river valleys, having cut through the escarpment mountains, are wide here, with extensive flood plains, like that of the Hoanib River west of the Giribes Plains. The gradient across the plains is gentle and the slowing waters after seasonal floods deposit rich layers of silt which eventually support a growth of vegetation. The silt layers dry and crack into delicate smooth-surfaced mosaics in which the spoor of birds and game are impressed and baked by the sun. Not all the rivers have wide

South of the Hoanib the country is more gently undulating, in a region of intensively folded schist hills which soon give way to the Uniab and Huab basins: the heartland, in scenery and atmosphere, of western Damaraland. The landscapes are formed by erosion of basalt lavas of the Stormberg series, also known as the Etendeka lavas. They are part of the same great outpouring that produced one of the largest lava fields known on earth, extending to the high Drakensberg of South Africa and beyond. The Etendeka lavas alone cover about 10 000 km². The weathered lava gives the rocks and gravel their characteristic reddish to purple colour, especially during droughts and the dry season when there is no grass, or that which remains is pale and tawny.

The lava landscape weathers into typical tabletop hills and mountains with gentle, extended talus slopes giving softness to the scene. The valley sides are gently sculpted, leading to shallow, wide valleys lower down the drainage lines. It is a country of far vistas — to the west lies the desert proper, to the east the distant phalanx of the escarpment. Towards the lower Huab, the valleys are broader and the tabletops not as densly clustered.

The rugged, desolate Ugab valley shows very different relief, with much deeper, steep-walled valleys cutting into rugged countryside, with low, steep scarps and steep pediment slopes.

South of the Ugab the dominant feature is the isolated granite massif of the Brandberg, which is a bulging intrusion through the Karoo rocks. Watercourses have eroded valleys on the outer edges of the massif which radiate in all directions. The highest dome of the Brandberg, known as Königstein, soars to 2 579 m and is the highest point in the country.

The Brandberg West area, which lies between the Brandberg and the coast, is a barren wasteland of volcanic basalt flats and pediments. Parallel ridges stretch for miles in a predominantly north-to-south orientation. The craters of several extinct volcanoes are found near by the Brandberg — Messum Crater to the

and shallow beds; the Uniab and its tributaries in particular have cut deep courses with steep-sided banks. The beds of these narrow-chanelled rivers are also gravel and pebble strewn, with occasional sandbanks on which stands of sedges or grasses grow.

In the northern part of the Kaokoland sector the hills are composed of highly metamorphosed sediments. In central Kaokoland the bedrock schists and gneiss are overlain by unfolded basalt which has been eroded into flat-topped mesas and pointed buttes, such as dominate the skyline in the region of the Khumib and Hoarusib rivers. Towards the Hoanib River, which is the boundary between Kaokoland and Damaraland, the relief is rugged and sharply incised with scattered rock outcrops, hills and mountains.

west, and to the north the cluster known as the Doros Craters.

South of the Brandberg the inner Namib is flat, gravel-covered plains stretching to the horizon. There is some variation in physiography in the catchment of the Omaruru River which is deeply incised and forms wide flood plains. South of the Omaruru the gravel flats continue to the Central Namib, broken only by isolated inselbergs.

The vegetation of the inner Namib is dominated by ephemeral grasses, annual and perennial herbs, with several species of shrubs and even a few species of trees. Much of the perennial vegetation is concentrated along drainage lines and on hills, and perennial grasses are only found on sandy soils such as in the Marienfluss valley. Large trees are only found along the major watercourses.

Soils are mostly shallow, poorly defined and unconsolidated, depending upon the nature of the parent material. The talus slopes nearer the escarpment mountains are usually strewn with rocks about 20–40 cm in diameter. The size of these loose rocks decreases as one moves westwards, so that on the eastern gravel plains the rocks are about 4–10 cm in diameter and on the gravel plains near the coast they are usually 1–4 cm.

The ephemeral grasses of the plains, such as *Stipagrostis hirtigluma*, dominate a sparse wispy grassland which appears rapidly after rain and may be absent in years when no rain falls. A few perennials like the gemsbok tail grass *(S. hochstetterana)* and *S. uniplumis* also occur. The ephemeral shaving brush grass *(S. subacaulis)* produces masses of silvery inflorescences which, in the early morning or late afternoon light, give a silvery white sparkling sheen to the gravel plains. The seeds, with their silky awns, are tumbled along by the wind and collect in small depressions and against rocks to form fluffy soft masses. Another well-known ephemeral grass is *Enneapogon desvauxii*, which is also known as eight-day grass because it grows and sets seed rapidly after rain.

Woody plants — other than the ubiquitous mopane, which is found along most drainage lines — are rare in the inner Namib, but widely scattered solitary specimens of *Maerua schinzii* occur. Against the backdrop of the reddish purple rocks of Damaraland the pale, smooth greyish bark of these trees is striking. Even more characteristic than the maeruas are the dark greenish grey humps formed by large *Euphorbia damarana* clumps, which grow two or three metres high with a diameter of about four metres. In the rugged country of the Ugab valley the spiny blue-green stems of *Euphorbia virosa* are conspicuous features of the vegetation. Herbs such as *Geigeria ornativa* and *Petalidium halimoides* are also ephemeral and disappear with the grasses when the land dries out. Several small shrubs like *Monechma arenicola*, *Petalidium variabile*, and *Calicorema capitata* are typically also found on the gravel plains. *Acacia reficiens*, *Gossypium anomalum* and *Commiphora wildii* occur as small stunted shrubs, especially along drainage lines.

One of the most extraordinary plants on earth, *Welwitschia mirabilis*, is confined to the gravel plains of the inner Namib. This plant is the sole representative of an ancient family of gymnosperms (the cone-bearing plants) and is regarded much like the coelacanth as a living fossil. It is actually a dwarf tree which has gone underground to avoid the desiccating effects of the desert climate. It produces only two dark green, leathery leaves which grow from the stem and persist throughout the life of the plant, which may be as long as 2 000 years. The leaves are split and curled by the wind and get broken and tattered to give the characteristic appearance of a convoluted heap of leaves surrounding a stem. The welwitschias grow in scattered colonies, in a wide belt of the gravel plains from the Kuiseb River in the south to as far north as Angola. The welwitschia belt usually lies about 30–40 km inland from the coast. Some of the largest specimens known are found near the Messum Crater, just to the southwest of the Brandberg.

Within the inner Namib region there are

several areas with deep sandy soils which are typically wide flat valleys surrounded by high mountains. Examples are the Marienfluss, the Hartmann valley and the Giribes flats near Sesfontein. The vegetation of these areas is characterised by perennial grasslands with scattered trees. The dominant grasses are *Stipagrostis uniplumis*, *S. giessii*, *Eragrostis porosa* and *Schmidtia kalahariensis*. The grassland is rich in species, and at least 18 have been described as occurring there. Small herbs or forbs appear scattered among the grasses. The most conspicuous are *Monechma divaricatum*, *Kohautia angolensis*, *Mollugo cerviana* and *Indigofera charlierana*. Trees are nowhere abundant, but the mopane occurs scattered or in occasional small clumps usually only two or three metres high. Along the watercourses, like the Otjinjangi which runs the length of the Marienfluss, typically riverine trees occur.

Apart from the breathtaking beauty of the Marienfluss its most striking feature is the occurrence of circular patches of bare ground in the grassland. These patches vary from two to five metres in diameter, and on sloping ground they are usually oval in shape with the long axis of the oval aligned with the slope. These patches of apparently sterile soil are fringed by a dense growth of the grass *Stipagrostis giessii* standing about 10 cm taller than the surrounding *S. uniplumis*, thus accentuating the strange circles. The origin of these circles of bare ground (which also occur in the Giribes area) was attributed by Ken Tinley to extinct termitaria from a formerly higher rainfall period. Excavations in some of these circles have not yet yielded any evidence to support this hypothesis. Another suggestion, by Professor Guillaume Theron, is that the patches were formed after the death of large *Euphorbia damarana* plants which formerly grew on those sites. These plants could have left toxic chemical substances in the soil after their remains decayed and this could inhibit the growth of other plants on that spot. This does not, however, explain why similar patches do not occur elsewhere in the presence of *E. damarana* — though soil type may be part of the explanation. The mystery persists.

The mountainous parts of the inner Namib support a sparse shrub savanna characterised by the presence of several commiphoras and the absence of mopane. The indicator species of this vegetation type are shrubby low-growing *Commiphora wildii*, *C. giessii*, *C. virgata*, *C. saxicola* and *C. kraeuseliana*. Two aloe species are also found in these hilly areas, *Aloe asperifolia* and *A. littoralis*. Scattered solitary trees are found, the most conspicuous being the star chestnut, *Sterculia africana*, which has a smooth silvery white bark, *Maerua schinzii*, and the shepherd's tree, *Boscia albitrunca*.

The best-developed savanna in the inner Namib region is found on the Otjiha plains, a few kilometres northeast of Orupembe. The soil is a deep red sand which supports a savanna growth dominated by the false umbrella thorn (*Acacia reficiens*) and the flood-plain acacia (*A. kirkii*), which grow to about three metres in height in a multistemmed shrubby growth form. There are very few shrubs and the ground cover is dominated by grasses. The Otjiha plains are a wet-season grazing area and have been heavily over-grazed by game and domestic stock over the years.

A largely mountainous and broken escarpment extends the full length of Kaokoland and Damaraland. Where it enters our region on the south bank of the Kunene it is marked by rugged mountain ranges. To the south it is little more than a raised platform. It separates the low-lying inner Namib plains from the highlands to the east. It is wild, arid and desolate country, lying between the 100 and 150 mm rainfall isohyets. In Kaokoland the escarpment zone lies between about 60 and 90 km from the coast. South of the Hoanib, in Damaraland, it gradually flattens and trends westward, reaching a distance of only 50 km from the coast in the Arandis area of southern Damaraland.

In the north the escarpment is spectacularly defined by the western edge of the Otjihipa mountains, forming an almost unbroken wall of rock rising steeply from the floor of the Marienfluss to a height of 1 500 metres. The Otjihipa escarpment extends for 80 km south of the Kunene. Then, just north of Otjiha, it is broken by the Otjinjangi River which, after cutting through the mountains from the east, turns sharply to the northwest. It then runs the length of the Marienfluss to join the Kunene through a small gorge cut off from the Hartmann Mountains a few kilometres from Otjinungwa.

Between Otjiha and Omatati on the Hoarusib River the mountains are broken and cut by branches of the Khumib River and the Hoarusib itself. Some of these watercourses have cut major valleys into the escarpment, others flow through rock-filled gorges and ravines. South of the Hoarusib the escarpment once again forms an unbroken chain for 40 km before it is cut by the spectacular gorge of the Gomatum River. It then continues almost unbroken to the dolomite mountains west of Sesfontein and the valley and gorges of the Hoanib River.

The crumbling ruins of an old German fort still stand at Sesfontein, which lies among rounded dolomite and limestone hills in the wide valley of the Hoanib River. The Lower Beesvlakte is a wide valley system which was formed below the scarp face of the eastern edge of the calcrete plateau. The rolling hills of the area east of the Lower Beesvlakte are separated by alluvial valleys, whose source material originated when erosion cut into the plateau. The valleys here are characteristically so wide that they can be described as plains. Such also are the plains around Sesfontein and Warmquelle. In places the topography is steep and there are impressive broken limestone cliffs. To the east of the Warmquelle valley the Hoanib cuts through the mountains which form part of the escarpment to the eastern plateau in an impressive narrow, steep-walled, twisting and winding gorge known as the Kowarib Schlucht. This rocky barrier separates the Warmquelle valley from the Lower Beesvlakte. Several watercourses join the Hoanib at the mouth of the Lower Bees-vlakte valley, among them the Ombonde, which rises near Kamanjab and is a major tributary of the Hoanib.

There are strong springs at Sesfontein and Warmquelle. As the name implies, there are six eyes at Sesfontein, which deliver a combined volume of 95 000 litres per hour. Unfortunately, the springs have been canalised and piped and they no longer flow as they used to. This has resulted in the dying back of several of the larger old fig trees which were a feature of Sesfontein and were dependent on the water.

Water is generally scarce in the escarpment zone between the Kunene and Hoanib, but there are a vital few small springs and water-holes.

The escarpment zone mountains of Kaokoland are characterised by steep and rugged topography, with huge expanses of bare, sunbaked rock, jumbled boulders and talus rubble (left behind by ancient glaciers of the last great Ice Age). The internal folding of the escarpment mountain rocks has contributed to the formation of gorges, cut into mountains, which often open into isolated, dry valleys, completely cut off from the Namib plains.

South of the Hoanib the escarpment occupies a broader, but less clearly defined region. The country is still mountainous, but the mountains are further apart, some isolated, and there are no extensive ranges. The mountain areas are also cut into by broad valleys and extensive plains. In the Hoanib drainage basin there is a high proportion of calcrete in the upper reaches of the valleys, while the lower reaches consist of deeper alluvial and colluvial deposits.

The Uniab drainage basin lies across the watershed from the Hoanib basin. Here the escarpment zone is hardly recognisable, for the individual mountains are again huge and prominent with flat tabletops and steep pediment slopes which extend into broad gently incised valleys and gently rolling plains. Striking topography is seen in the Uniab Canyons — a series of tributaries of the Uniab which have cut deep-sided ravines into the underlying bedrock.

The catchment of the Huab and its tributaries lies in a very broken, rocky area of mountains and hills, with extensive scree slopes which are hot, barren and devoid of plant life. It is not all so rugged though, for there are also gently undulating plains and smooth, wide valleys in this area. Some such are found near Twyfelfontein, where one would scarcely believe that one was in anything like an escarpment zone.

South of Twyfelfontein the escarpment zone disappears and there is a direct transition from the inner Namib plains to the eastern highlands along the Ugab River valley. The nearby Doros Craters provide some topographical re-

lief. Just southeast of the craters lies a large dunefield, outliers of which create sandy slopes to the barren hills near Twyfelfontein and the Burnt Mountain. This mountain, also the remains of an extinct, primeval volcano, rises about 200 metres above the plains. It is striking because the basically reddish coloured rock, typical of the entire area, is streaked by bands of black, white and grey. The dunefield is made up of a gently undulating sand plain with parallel dunes. The hollows between the sand dunes occasionally show exposures of calcrete.

South of the dunefield and the isolated Brandberg massif, the escarpment is not clearly distinguishable. The area around Uis and the Omaruru River between Nasutosub and Rietkuil and south to the southern border of Damaraland differs little from the southern plains, with frequent granite and schist exposures and odd scattered small hills. The land slopes gently towards the coast.

The mountains of the escarpment zone in Kaokoland are extremely rugged, with steep slopes, deep gorges and narrow razor-back ridges. This creates a diversity of microhabitats brought about by aspect, slope, shading, geology and the varying effectiveness of rainfall and water runoff. This diversity results in great variation in the composition of plant communities. South of the Hoanib, geologically different parent material with other weathering characteristics has given rise to very different landscapes. The Damaraland mountains have gentler topography and are generally flat-topped. Plant communities are more uniform over larger areas. As a general rule the plant species diversity is greatest in the north and the number of species declines rapidly as one moves southwards. The escarpment shows the transition from the vegetation of the higher-rainfall eastern plateau regions to that of the inner Namib.

The transition is illustrated not only by species composition of the plant communities, but also by growth form within a single species. Thus the mopanes and sterkbos are found as trees three to five metres high on the eastern side of the escarpment mountains, but are dwarfed to one or two metres high on the west. Likewise, *Commiphora virgata* is a small single-stemmed tree up to three metres high in the escarpment zone, but is only found as a low-growing multi-stemmed shrub in the inner Namib.

The vegetation of the westernmost escarpment region is a low, open savanna, dominated by single-stemmed dwarf mopane trees. Scattered among the mopanes are shrubby trumpet thorn *(Catophractes alexandri)* and sterkbos, and the ever-present dark *Euphorbia damarana* bushes. The shrub layer is dominated by species like *Petalidium variabile* and several other members of the same genus. Other important shrubs are *Adenolobus pechuelii* and *Bonamia schizantha*. On steep rocky slopes *Sterculia africana*, the Brandberg acacia *(Acacia montis-usti)* and various commiphoras are found. Most of the grasses are annuals which are soon grazed and trampled after rains. Common grass species are *Schmidtia kalahariensis, Stipagrostis giessii, Enneapogon cenchroides* and *Kaokochloa nigrirostris.*

To the east, where rainfall is higher, the dominant woody plants are *Commiphora multijuga* and *C. virgata*, together with mopane and sterkbos. *Euphorbia guerichiana* is particularly abundant in the Otjihipa mountains in the north of Kaokoland. Along watercourses which cut through the rugged terrain the dominant trees are mopane, the scented thorn *(Acacia nilotica* subsp. *kraussiana)*, the ana tree or winter thorn *(A. albida)* and leadwood *(Combretum imberbe).*

The shrub layer is also richer than that of the plant communities to the west and contains species that are more usually found in the higher rainfall regions across to the east of the subcontinent. Among them are the Kalahari christmas tree *(Dichrostachys cinerea)*, flame acacia *(Acacia ataxacantha)*, *A. senegal*, *Grewia bicolor* and *G. villosa*. A common shrub is *Elephantorrhiza suffriticosa*. Herbs and grasses are

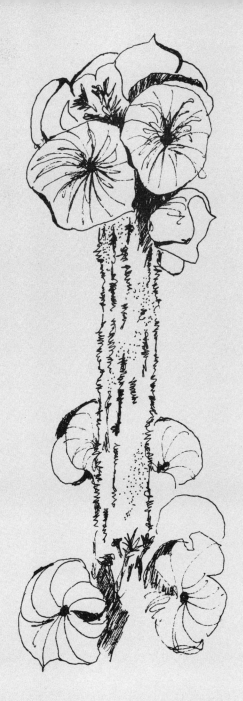

generally poorly represented, and only conspicuous after rain. *Aristida rhiniochloa* and *Entoplacamia aristulata* are the most abundant grasses, though many other species are also present. Small forbs like *Cleome suffruticosa, Crotolaria damarensis* and *Hermannia amabilis* are common.

Along the upper reaches of the Hoarusib, west of the Steilrand mountains, there are some extensive areas of dwarf tree savanna on calcrete soils, dominated by mopane and sterkbos. This area is heavily overgrazed by

11

domestic stock and the grass layer is consequently dominated by *Schmidtia kalahariensis*. On the deeper soils near Sesfontein and Warmquelle the trees are much taller and umbrella thorns *(Acacia tortilis)* with a mean height of 12 metres are co-dominant with tall mopane trees. The mustard bush *(Salvadora persica)* is common in the shrub stratum. The camel thorn tree *(Acacia erioloba)*, which is typical of arid areas throughout the southwestern part of the subcontinent, is also common on these plains. This veld type being fairly productive and close to permanent water, it has been devastated by the cumulative effect of overgrazing and over-browsing by cattle and goats. Much of this area has been reduced to desperate conditions, with bare powdery sand and dead mopanes.

The vegetation of the northeastern escarpment zone, as exemplified in the Baynes and Otjihipa mountains and also the mountains between Warmquelle and Sesfontein, contains many species of plants that are either endemic to the Kaokoveld or representative of the eastern mesic flora. Among the latter categories are the baobab *(Adansonia digitata)*, red

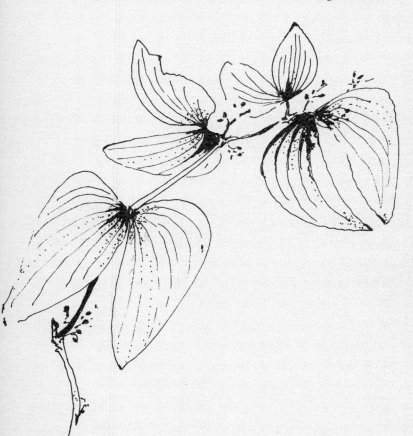

bushwillow *(Combretum apiculatum)*, tambotie, African wattle *(Peltophorum africanum)*, white syringa, jakkalsbessie *(Diospyros mespiliformis)* and the marula *(Sclerocarya birrea)*. The shrub and herb layer is equally rich in species of the higher rainfall regions. A striking feature of the mountain savannas is the importance of aspect in determining the dominant species. This is well illustrated in the Baynes mountains, where *Acacia mellifera* is dominant on north-facing slopes, *Commiphora multijuga* dominates the west-facing slopes and *Acacia ataxacantha* is dominant on south-facing slopes.

The Kaokoveld endemic plants include *Aloe mendesi*, *Rhigozum virgatum*, *Euphorbia kaokoensis* and *E. subsalsa* subsp. *fluvialis*, which are mostly restricted to the Baynes mountains. *Euphorbia eduardoi* can be found in the Otjihipa mountains and *Sesamothamnus benguellensis* is more widespread. To the south are endemics like *Kirkia dewinteri*, *Acacia robynsiana*, *A. montis-usti* and *Aloe dewinteri*.

The Beesvlakte plains east of Warmquelle, like the Marienfluss, are a wide valley surrounded by high mountains. These plains lie at an altitude of 600–800 metres and receive rainfall of 250–300 mm per year. This has resulted in the natural vegetation being a predominantly perennial grassland. The dominant grasses are *Stipagrostis giessii* and *S. hirtigluma*, and the basal cover, especially in the south, is very good. The central section of the plains, where windmills have led to year-round grazing by domestic stock, has been heavily overgrazed. The grassland in this area has been replaced by a dwarf shrub community reminiscent of the Karoo and dominated by *Leucosphaera bainesii* and *Monechma salsola*. There are no longer any trees to be found in the overgrazed zone but in the south mopanes are common along drainage lines. Along the larger watercourses ana trees, camel thorn and umbrella thorn are common. The shrub layer is dominated by small mopanes up to 1,5 metres high and to the east *Grewia flava* is locally abundant.

The eastern highlands of Kaokoland lie at an altitude of 1 000–1 300 metres, with mountains rising another 500–800 metres above the generally flat high plains. Most of the region is east of the 250 mm rainfall isohyet.

Mountains and valley systems divide the highlands into three distinct physiographic regions. The northern part, also referred to as the Ovahimba highlands, is drained by the Omuhonga, Otjitanga and Ondoto river systems, which are tributaries of the Kunene. Topography is very rugged, with steep-sided hills and valleys and deep gorges. The central areas form the upper catchment of the Hoarusib, which originates near Opuwo and the foot of the Steilrand Mountains. The southern part of the highlands is dissected by the northern tributaries of the Hoanib River. Much of the east and southeast of this region lies on Otavi dolomite covered by a mantle of reddish or yellow-brown Kalahari sands of variable depth, which stretch eastwards to form the Ovambo plain. The limestone plateau landscape is generally gently undulating, with little surface relief. The porous nature of dolomite reduces water run-off, thus denying a major form of weathering, as well as giving rise to numerous springs.

The highlands of Kaokoland fall into two bioclimatic regions: the central drainage basins, characterised by gneiss and quartzite and lying between the 150 and 250 mm isohyets, and the eastern highland plateau, with dolomite and limestone geology and rainfall of 250–350 mm per annum.

The eastern highland plateau of the Kaokoveld extends along the Ovamboland border, abutting the Kalahari basin — the major physiographic region of southern and central Africa. Generally flat and covered by Kalahari sand, the plateau adjoins the Owambo plain along the centre, and the Etosha National Park in the southeast between Otjikowares and Onaiso. This sand plateau is also known as the kalk plateau, an obvious reference to the calcrete layer under the sand — a feature typical of much of the central part of Namibia. The sandveld stretches westwards to the Joubert Mountains and the dolomite hills north and east of Opuwo.

Most of the sandveld has small local grass-covered drainage systems, which flood into pans and vleis during the rains. These seasonally flooded pans are a feature of Ovamboland, where they are known as *oshanas*, and some hold water for several months after the rains. Most of the sandveld area is, however, without natural water sources. Most perennial springs, like Ombombo Owambo, are the focal points of small settlements. Elsewhere boreholes have been sunk to provide water for people and animals.

The northern Etoto plains form the northern extension of the kalk plateau, stretching to the foothills of the Ehombo Mountains. This northern sector exhibits more distinct topography than the rest of the sandveld, with low rocky ridges separated by gently undulating broad valleys.

The central Opuwo region falls within the higher rainfall region of Kaokoland, but lies west of, and below, the escarpment of the eastern sandveld. Its main topographic features include a series of very wide valleys and plains, enclosed by mountain ranges and steep hills, south of the Steilrand Mountains and northeast of the Giraffen Mountains.

The low scarp edge of the eastern sandveld is very distinct. The calcrete plateau has, through erosion and weathering, provided the material for these lower-lying calcrete plains. Typical of this region are the flat, treeless plains seen around Opuwo. The largest of the Kaokoveld's seasonal rivers, the Hoarusib, rises close to Opuwo.

Higher than the eastern sandveld plateau and the Opuwo region, the Kaoko Otavi–Ombombo valley area is characterised by a series of north–south orientated wide valleys, from which rise steep, rolling dolomite and limestone hills. This region lies between the

nioides and *Combretum apiculatum*. On the deeper yellowish or reddish sandy soils *Terminalia sericea* is dominant and mopane, Kalahari apple-leaf (*Lonchocarpus nelsii*) and camel thorn trees are co-dominants. On the skeletal soils characteristic of calcrete outcroppings, *Sesamothamnus guerichii* is dominant, with stunted mopane trees. The shrub layer is characterised by multi-stemmed shrub mopane with *Grewia flava* and some acacia species. As there are few waterpoints in the area so far, grazing pressure in the past has not been high and the understory of herbs and grasses is well developed. These, together with the abundant shrubs up to 1,5 metres high, give a dense, closed, almost thicket-like appearance to the sandveld vegetation.

The grasses are strongly perennial and the dominants are *Schmidtia pappophoroides, Eragrostis denudata, Stipagrostis uniplumis* and *Bothriochloa radicans*. Fire is a regular occurrence, as this is the only area of the Kaokoveld where sufficient plant material is available in the dry season to allow burning. Another striking feature is the occurrence of tall termite mounds on the plateau — a feature not found in the drier areas. The termitaria have strongly associated plant species which benefit from the greater organic content of the termite mound soils. Mopanes growing on the mounds are also much taller (10–15 metres) than in the surrounding woodland. Other tree species associated with the termitaria are *Albizia anthelmintica*, buffalo thorn (*Ziziphus mucronata*) and African wattle. Grasses such as *Fingerhuthia africana, Setaria verticillata* and *Panicum coloratum* are associated with termite mound soils as well as with turf soils around the numerous seasonal pans on the sandveld.

Joubert Mountains, to the east, and the escarpment mountains, to the west. Hills and ridges are usually rounded and there are few higher than 1 600 metres.

To the south, in the mountains above Sesfontein, the landscape is more rugged, as also to the west where the hills merge into the folded quartzitic escarpment mountains. Waterholes and springs are numerous in these dolomite hills, the most generous being Kaoko Otavi itself, which delivers over 200 000 litres per hour. Other strong springs are found at Okorosave and Ombombo.

The long-term mean rainfall of the eastern sandveld is about 400 mm per annum. The vegetation is a fairly dense woodland or tree savanna with a clearly differentiated shrub layer and a dense field layer. The plant communities are all dominated by mopane trees. On the areas of shallow or stony ground the co-dominants with mopane are *Terminalia pru-*

The central drainage basin of the Kaokoveld can be divided into a northern and a southern half. The northern, or Ovahimba, highlands area is bounded to north, east and west by the Kunene, the calcrete plateau of the eastern highlands, and the escarpment, and to the south by the Tonnesen and Giraffen Mountains. It includes the catchments of three of the larger Kaokoland rivers. Flowing north and east to the Kunene are the Omuhonga and Ondoto rivers, whose catchments are separated by the Zebra Mountains, and on the southern side of the Steilrand Mountains are the headwaters of the Hoarusib.

The landscapes of the basins are wide, undulating plains with very broken topography and prominently incised drainage lines. The quartzite flat-topped eastern Baynes Mountains, at 1 600 metres, with peaks above 2 000 metres, form the northwestern corner of this region. To the west, across the deeply incised valley of the Otjipemba River, lie the Otjihipa Mountains, which are part of the escarpment.

The Zebra Mountains are so-called because the steep slopes of this range are striped. Vertical bands of densely bushed vegetation alternate with bands of bare, loosely jumbled black boulders. These mountains are composed of anorthosite, which is extremely hard and resistant to weathering. Thus the Zebra Mountains, in geomorphological terms, represent a much 'younger' erosion stage than most other ranges in the regions, with very narrow, steep-sided valleys, particularly to the east.

Prominent ridges and mountains add to the impression of rugged, broken country on the Ovahimba highlands. The Ehomba range, which reaches 1 860 metres, and the smaller Etoroha ridge run east to west, while the Steilrand Mountains (1 964 m) lie slightly more southeast to northwest. Isolated rocky koppies and granite inselbergs occur widely in the north and west.

Although the rivers carry surface water only after rain, there is a constant flow of water under the sand. Where rock sills cut across riverbeds this subterranean water is forced up and appears on the surface as natural springs, well scattered along the river courses. Other strong perennial springs also occur on the sides of mountains.

The Ovahimba highlands in the north of Kaokoland probably receive more than 300 mm annual rainfall and have generally shallow, reddish coloured sandy loam soils. The vegetation throughout is characterised by the presence of one or more of three dominant tree species, mopane, sterkbos and red bush-willow. The vegetation varies from savanna with widely spaced trees to a fairly dense woodland with tall trees. There are several subtypes of vegetation which have developed in response to different soils.

The plains and valleys of the north, with shallow stony loam to sandy loam soils, support a fairly homogeneous tree savanna in which mopane and terminalia are most abundant, and with red bushwillow widespread and locally abundant. Baobabs and other tree species are also widely scattered. In low-lying areas with deeper soils the species diversity declines and mopanes occur in almost pure stands of well-formed trees about eight metres high. On exceptionally shallow and stony soils *Acacia reficiens* becomes dominant and the mopanes are somewhat stunted.

The shrub stratum is characterised by *Catophractes alexandri* on shallow and calcrete soils and by *Grewia bicolor* and *Rhigozum brevispinosum* on deeper soils, but there are also many other shrub species present. Around waterpoints where heavy overgrazing and trampling by domestic stock has occurred the shrub *Pechuel-Loeschia leubnitziae* is dominant.

The higher rainfall, access to the Kunene in the dry season and the many waterpoints have resulted in most of the northern highlands being permanently occupied by cattle-keeping Himba. Overgrazing and trampling by livestock is consequently widespread and has resulted in extensive surface and donga erosion. The grass stratum has also been largely changed, perennials have been replaced by annuals, the dominant species over large areas is now the pioneer *Schmidtia kalahariensis*. On stony ground *Stipagrostis hirtigluma* is prominent, while protected sites under trees and bushes still carry *Enneapogon cenchroides*, *Aristida adscensionis* and *Rhyn-*

chelytrum villosum. Forbs are common and abundant after rain.

Several species of commiphoras are characteristically prominent components of the vegetation of the hills in the highlands, as also in the escarpment zone. *Commiphora multijuga, C. glaucescens* and *C. mollis* are the most common. The white syringa *(Kirkia acuminata)* and other typically hill-species such as *Sesamothamnus benguellensis, Pachypodium lealii* and star chestnut also occur. The composition of the grass flora of the hills also differs and the dominant is *Microchloa caffra.*

On deeper sandy soils, and among the granite hills of the northeast as well as the Ehomba mountains, the tree savanna is characterised by *Hippocratea africana* and *Pterocarpus antunesii* in addition to mopane. Other trees more typical of the eastern sandveld are also mixed into these savanna communities. Among the most prominent are Kalahari apple leaf, blade thorn *(Acacia fleckii)* and bird plum *(Berchemia discolor).* Typical large shrubs are cork bush *(Mundulea sericea)* and lavender croton *(Croton subgratissimus).* On granite outcrops to the west, where it is drier, *Cissus nymphaeifolia* and *Hexalobis monopeltus* occur.

The second main drainage system, the southern dolomite hills, forms the drainage basin of the Upper Beesvlakte system, a series of interlocked valleys below the western scarp of the calcrete plateau. The valleys are separated by low, rolling hills and their floors contain deep alluvial and colluvial material eroded away from the eastern plateau. At places the Upper Beesvlakte is wide enough to be considered a plain, and there are extensive calcrete flats on the valley floor. The Beesvlakte is drained by the Ombonde River, a major tributary of the Hoanib.

Immediately south of the Ombonde, around Palmfontein, are rolling schist hills interspaced by wide valleys, which give way to gravel plains with scattered granite/schist koppies. South of the Huab, around Khorixas, the administrative centre of Damaraland, the landscape is similar to the Upper Beesvlakte: it lies just below the scarp of the kalk plateau, which extends into Damaraland east of Khorixas. It is country of steep rocky slopes and a multitude of shallow drainage lines, giving the hills a rolling appearance.

Southeast of Twyfelfontein are gently undulating gravel plains with scattered granite koppies, where the rocks are almost bare of vegetation. Upland sections to the east are characterised by shallow red soil with granite boulders and outcrops. To the west, along the upper tributaries of the Huab and Ugab, soils are deeper and there are calcrete outcrops.

Still further south, the landscape is dominated by intensively folded schists of the Damara system, into which younger granites have intruded to form spectacular inselbergs like the Gross Spitskoppe. The country for miles around is gently undulating plains, from which granite spires tower up to 1 728 metres, creating a scenic masterpiece.

The soils of this region are generally shallow, greyish loam types with abundant calcrete outcrops in the north. Deeper, brownish, sandy loam soils are found to the east. In general the hill areas are characterised by stony shallow soils and the drainage lines by deep soils. As can be expected from such a large area, there are many local influences on the vegetation and many subtypes can be recognised. The typical vegetation of the area is a tree savanna formed by mopane and *Terminalia prunioides* trees, which are fairly closely spaced and vary in height from about five metres in the east to about three and a half metres in the west. Though several other tree species are found, they are usually well scattered. The most common of these are red bushwillow, common commiphora *(Commiphora pyracanthoides),* shepherd's tree and *Boscia foetida.* On the deeper soils towards the eastern edge of this region tambotie is well distributed though sparse. In the extreme south, in the Omaruru catchment, mopanes disappear and *Acacia reficiens, A. erubescens, A. senegal* and *A. tortilis* are dominant.

16

The hills typically support several commiphoras, including *Commiphora crenato-serrata* as well as the African moringo (*Moringa ovalifolia*), mountain albizia (*Albizia brevifolia*) and other species. The north-to-south orientated valleys of the Ombonde area show an interesting arrangement of plant communities with umbrella thorn and buffalo thorn (*Ziziphus mucronata*) dominant in the valleys where no mopane occurs, but mopane dominates on the intervening ridges. The absence of mopane in the valleys is thought to be caused by frost. Around Opuwo there are areas with few trees and the dominant vegetation is a dwarf shrubveld, mostly of *Petalidium rossmannianum* and *Hirpicium gorteroides*. This community is thought to have been caused by overgrazing, as it was traditionally known as grassveld.

Unlike the vegetation of the Ovahimba highlands, the central drainage basin savanna has a very well-developed shrub stratum, which is dominated by shrub mopane. Other plant communities are similar to those of the north, though local areas of dominance of one species or another are found, usually determined by soil factors. Throughout the area the shrub *Pechuel- Loeschia leubnitziae* and the forb *Tribulus zeyheri* are indicators of overgrazing and trampling and testimony to the decline in veld productivity. Most of the grasses and forbs are annuals and have a brief period of abundance during and after rains. Common grasses are *Pogonarthria fleckii*, *Eragrostis annulata*, *Aristida meridionalis* and *Enneapogon cenchroides*. In the areas further from water, and consequently less heavily used by cattle, a wide variety of perennial grasses may still be found.

The major rivers of the Kaokoveld all flow from east to west — from areas of higher rainfall through areas of decreasing rainfall until they end in the desert dunes of the Namib. From time to time the Hoarusib reaches the sea. Only the Kunene is perennial

and the mouth at Foz do Cunene is always open. The tributaries of the Kunene flow northwards; the tributaries of the other rivers trend to the west.

The importance of the Kaokoveld rivers lies not only in that they carry water into the desert in surface flow or under the sand, but that they support a chain of vegetation typical of the high-rainfall areas and extend the range of plants, and all the many forms of animal life which depend upon them, far into the inner Namib and the coastal desert itself. Many of the most important fountains and waterholes of the Kaokoveld are found in riverbeds where some rock obstruction forces the water to the surface. Some of these are Springbokwasser in a branch of the Koichab, Auses in the Hoanib, Purros in the Hoarusib and Okau in the Munutum. These fountains provide water for the animals, but the plants, provided their roots can reach deep enough, can tap water anywhere along the length of the riverbed. This explains the characteristic line of trees growing along the banks of the watercourses in areas which are otherwise devoid of trees.

The northward-flowing rivers that drain into the Kunene, such as the Omuhonga, Ondoto, Otjitanga and Heowa, as well as the Kunene itself, support a more tropical flora than the other Kaokoveld river systems. Many plant species are common to all the rivers, and are seldom found away from watercourses. Some of these are ana trees, camel thorn, leadwood, *Combretum wattii*, the makalani palm (*Hyphaene petersiana*), tamarisk, which in parts of South Africa is still known by its Nama name of 'abiquas', the mustard bush and *Euclea pseudebena*.

The shrub layer of the riverine vegetation may form locally dense thickets such as the tamarisk and *Salvadora persica* thickets of the Uniab River. The most common grasses in the riverbeds are *Stipagrostis namaquensis* and *Setaria finita*. The herb *Zygophyllum simplex* occurs in most riverbeds. On the wide floodplains of the Hoanib a dense growth of the shrubs *Salsola aphylla*, *Suaeda plumosa*, *Pluckea dioscorides* and *Sutera conescens* is found. The smaller westward-flowing rivers from the Omaruru northwards are characterised by a number of species not found in the larger rivers, such as *Balanites welwitschii* and *Parkinsonia africana*.

While the plant species composition changes along the length of the westward-flowing rivers, the rivers draining to the north generally support the same species along their entire length. These northward-flowing rivers, because they generally occur in more hospitable areas, are not as critical a food source for large mammals as are the rivers of the western desert regions. Large trees found only along the Kunene and its tributaries include jakkalsbessie, several species of figs such as *Ficus petersi*, *F. glumosa* and *F. sycomorus*, saffronwood (*Cassine transvaalensis*) and mountain albizia. Among the smaller trees are russet bushwillow (*Combretum hereroense*), bluebush (*Diospyros lycioides*), *Nuxia oppositifolia* and others. The shrub layer also in-

cludes some mesic species such as Transvaal gardenia (*Gardenia spatulifolia*), *Maytenus senegalensis* and *Ormocarpum kirkii*. The grasses, though heavily grazed by livestock, include *Cenchrus ciliarus*, *Cynodon dactylon*, *Echinochloa colonum* and *Panicum novemnerve*.

The Kunene has well-developed riverine vegetation between the Epupa Falls and Swartbooisdrift, where it is 80–150 metres wide with gently sloping banks. Dense stands of makalani palms and thickets of other woody plants are found. West of Swartboois the river is crowded into a narrow gorge between the Baynes and Otjihipa mountains on the south bank and the Tjamalindi mountains in Angola and there is very little riverine vegetation in this section. From Otjinungwa westwards the river widens, and although there is a fringe of vegetation it is not as diverse as that to the east. Dense reedbeds of *Phragmites australis* are common on the banks and islands in the east, and also far to the south along the Huab River.

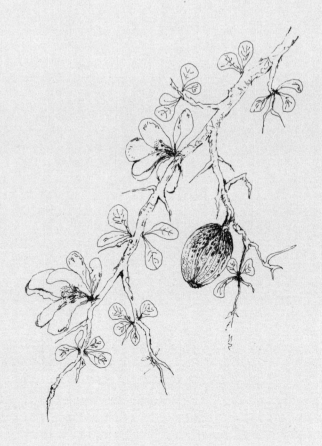

Animals

The Kaokoveld is a reservoir of biological diversity of a special kind, because its wealth of animal life survives in such an arid environment and not the kind of place normally associated with abundant animal life. The Kaokoveld is a centre of endemism and variety. There are nine endemic species of birds; an endemic subspecies of impala known as the blackfaced impala and at least one endemic lizard. The region is also a stronghold for the Damara dik-dik, which, in southern Africa, occurs in the Kaokoveld and limited surrounding country. The Kaokoveld and adjoining areas are the only part of southern Africa where the striped tree squirrel occurs, and it is one of the few areas in Africa that still have viable populations of both African elephants and black rhinoceros. More unusually, it is the only area on earth where these two pachyderms occur together with lions and giraffe in a desert environment.

The invertebrates of the Namib, and in particular the various forms of beetles dependent upon the sea fog, have been well studied at the Desert Research Station at Gobabeb, on the Kuiseb River. Study of the spiders, lizards, snakes and geckoes of the Central Namib (many of which are also to be found in the Kaokoveld) has also been promoted at Gobabeb.

It has, however, been the large mammals which have attracted the most interest, and which have been the focus and stimulus for the promotion of conservation activity in the Kaokoveld over the past few years. The flagship animals — those that serve most directly to illustrate the dangers facing the wilderness, and that invited the action — were the desert-dwelling elephant and black rhino. The giraffe and lions of the desert regions of the Kaokoveld also played a role. These four animals are normally associated with savannas and woodlands, where nature is more generous in providing food and water. To survive in the arid areas of the Kaokoveld they have had to evolve lifestyles which biologists have found to be complex illustrations of adaptability. These adaptations have affected the behaviour and possibly even the physiology of the animals. While there can be no serious intention of regarding these animals as taxonomic units or separate subspecies, they are for the most part populations that are ecologically isolated.

Large game populations existed in the Kaokoveld, and in particular in Kaokoland and western Damaraland, until the 1960s. From then on, the changed legal status of these areas, growing human populations and changing lifestyles among the people brought about by boreholes, roads, improved health and veterinary services, led to rapid overstocking, degradation of grazing and increased competition with wildlife for pasture and water. Game was driven out of the populated areas as surely by the cattle, sheep and goats, as by illegal hunting. The game herds were eliminated from the eastern plateau areas or forced to move into the less attractive and less productive habitats of the lower rainfall areas to the west. As veld conditions deteriorated in the east, so the westward pressure on the wildlife increased. Furthermore, particularly in Damaraland, veterinary fences stopped the seasonal movements of animals to and from the higher rainfall areas in the east and the western desert regions.

The larger plains game like springbok, gemsbok, Hartmann's mountain zebra and Burchell's zebra had previously been able to make the best use of available resources by moving westwards to areas where rain had fallen during the summer, and then eastwards during the dry season. The antelope moved between the plains and the adjacent mountains, the zebra as far east as Etosha. Local concentrations on the gravel plains might be seen wherever rainfall and consequent grass growth allowed. Declining forage quality and availability of water (as determined both by moisture content of the forage and drinking water) drove the animals eastwards and to the vicinity of permanent waterholes in the dry season. Likewise, when people and livestock were few they could move into areas where rain had fallen and utilise the grasslands on an annual basis. As waterholes dried up and forage declined, livestock and people moved towards permanent water sources and traditional dry-season grazing areas.

The disruption of time-honoured, ecologically evolved systems of land use by wildlife and people is not unique to the Kaokoveld. These same processes have already run their course in the Sahel and East Africa. The disastrous consequences for people, livestock, wildlife and plant resources are well documented. Local extinction of wild animals, the death of livestock, people facing famine and malnutrition, and the advance of the desert into areas once productive are certain consequences of the recent trends.

International agencies are now mounting expensive efforts to counter the desertification process in the Sahel zone, but the damage has been done and it is largely irreversible in the short term. Sadly, there is every indication that Kaokoland and parts of Damaraland are headed on the same course.

There are several sources of information on the mammals of the Kaokoveld in the accounts of early travellers and explorers. In this century the landmark work was by Captain G. C. Shortridge, for some years mammalogist at the Kaffrarian Museum in King William's Town. His work is contained in the two-volume classic *Mammals of South West Africa*, which appeared in 1934.

While containing much valuable information, these works were not comprehensive. Recent contributions to our knowledge of the distribution and ecology of mammals of the area have been made by Garth Owen-Smith, who was agricultural officer for the territory of Kaokoland from 1968 to 1970 and has worked again in the area for the past six years. The collaborative work of Dr Eugene Joubert and Peter Mostert of the Directorate of Nature Conservation, which was published in 1975, is also a valuable source of information. P. J. 'Slang' Viljoen carried out intensive detailed surveys on the distribution of the large mammals of Kaokoland from 1975 to 1977.

These works, together with several others such as the recent publication on the elephants of Kaokoland and Damaraland by Slang Viljoen, and the reports of Blythe Loutit's work on black rhino in Damaraland, provide the foundation for an overview of the status and distribution of the large mammals of the Kaokoveld over the past half century.

A checklist of the Kaokoveld's mammals is given at the end of the book.

The desert-dwelling elephants, together with the black rhino, are the jewels in the crown of the Kaokoveld. Without them the beauty of this wilderness would be sadly demeaned. They add a dimension of grandeur and excitement to the landscape. They are also an integral part of the unique ecosystem which has evolved here. The elephants have an influence on plants and other animals which is little understood or recognised. They are not a separate subspecies of the African elephant *(Loxodonta africana)*, but belong to the savanna elephant subspecies *(L. a. africana)* as opposed to the forest elephant *(L. a. cyclotis)*. They are, however, an ecotype — a population that has adapted to survival in the desert by behaviour, tradition and perhaps also physiology.

Evidence from rock engravings and written records indicates that there have been elephant in the desert regions of the Kaokoveld since time immemorial. They were not driven into the desert by recent human disturbance and pressure, as has been suggested by some observers. Apart from the definite records of their presence in the desert before 1880, their behaviour and biology indicates that they have lived there for a long time. The desert elephants were also, until fairly recent times, in contact with other elephant populations whose distribution was continuous to the east into Etosha and northwards

into Angola. Earlier than that they would have been the western edge of a blanket of elephants which covered the entire subcontinent.

However, elephants do not wander around at random. There is a very definite social spacing of herds. Research in the Kruger National Park has shown that groupings of related breeding herds known as clans occupy distinct clan ranges. Though adjoining clans may have contact in overlapping boundary zones the bulk of the clan range is used exclusively by clan members. In the Kruger, clan ranges vary from 126 to 987 km² in size, with a mean size of 452 km². In general, where the habitat is better and food resources are more abundant the clan range is smaller than in areas of poorer habitat with less food resources. Slang Viljoen's studies on the Kaokoveld elephants confirm this general pattern and, as might be expected, the clan ranges in the desert are considerably larger. They range from 1 700 to nearly 3 000 km², with a mean home range size of 1 871 km².

Elephants have a matriarchal society, and herds are made up of cows and their offspring. Bulls are not permanent members of the herds. At maturity they drift off into bull ranges which are the equivalent of clan ranges. Bulls are usually the exclusive occupants of such ranges, which in the Kruger average out at about 660 km². In the Kaokoveld the bull ranges average 2 698 km².

The bulls from a particular clan generally drift off at sexual maturity into the same bull ranges as their relatives. Occasionally they move to other bull ranges, from where they make contact with cows of unrelated clans, but they are more likely to stay in bull ranges close to their maternal clan range, and hence more likely to breed with local cows. In this way, local gene pools are developed, with their own characteristics. So, for example, the Addo elephants differ in some respects from Kruger elephants with whom they would have been connected via many intermediate populations in the past. Likewise, the desert elephant gene pool has developed its own characteristics. These could range from cultural traits such as knowledge of the local environment to physical characteristics such as the sharply upcurved tusks of the bulls. Reproductive isolation of such populations is, however, seldom complete. Indeed, it has been suggested that the phenomenon of musth — where bulls become aggressive and travel long distances away from their normal range in search of cows — is a mechanism which has evolved to ensure the exchange of genetic material between elephant populations. We know that musth occurs in Kaokoveld elephant bulls and, therefore, some genetic contact with other populations seems assured.

The Kaokoveld elephants appear to be very well adapted to living under the particular ecological conditions of the desert. They routinely move great distances between feeding grounds and the scattered waterholes where they drink during the dry season, distances of up to 70 km being regularly traversed. Slang Viljoen recorded a maximum straight-line distance of one such journey of 195 kilometres, and a record return trip of 390 kilometres. Such long treks require the expenditure of a great deal of energy, which must then be provided from their scarce food sources. They are, therefore, necessarily frugal in their drinking habits and only drink every third or fourth day, thereby saving on their energy needs. Elsewhere, including Etosha, elephants normally drink every day.

The desert elephants feed on a wide range of plants, and like elephants elsewhere they take leaves, shoots, bark, flowers, fruit, bulbs, tubers and roots as well as grass and sedges. They have distinct and practical seasonal feeding preferences. During the rains they tend to use more grass, which is then more abundantly available, and during the dry season they concentrate on browse. This allows the woody plants a measure of respite for recovery during the summer.

They are careful feeders, and in this they are quite unlike most other elephants that have been studied. The Kaokoveld elephants break branches like other elephants, but not nearly to the same extent as can be seen in the Kruger. They seldom fell trees as other elephants do. They also do not debark trees to the same degree as elsewhere. This care in husbanding their food resources can be seen as behaviour necessary to ensure survival in an environment where woody plants are few and far between. There is, therefore, little of the 'elephant damage' or 'elephant impact' that has been recorded from other areas to be seen in the Kaokoveld.

Because their food is so widely scattered the desert elephants are required to spend more time, and energy, on the move in search of food. Their daily movements cover about 26 km, according to Viljoen. Elephants in the Kruger, Addo or Knysna, by contrast, seldom move further than 5–10 km per day when not disturbed. The desert elephants, like most of the other mammals, birds and insects, are heavily dependent on the vegetation of the riverbeds for food. However, even in the Hoanib, where they occasionally ringbark ana trees, the percentage of elephant-damaged trees that will probably die is less than a third of the percentage of immature, established trees that are able to replace them. This is the situation now, when the elephant population is a remnant one; yet the evidence indicates that the equilibrium between elephants and trees was equally stable in the past when there were far more elephants living in the Kaokoveld.

That the desert elephants are living below the ecological carrying capacity of their environment is borne out by events during the prolonged and severe drought of 1979–82. During this time, when an estimated 80 per cent of all the wild ungulates died, not one desert elephant death was ascribed to drought. Further to the east, however, at Palmfontein, the death of five elephants of the eastern population was ascribed to the drought. These elephants are in regular contact with the Etosha population and are probably not as

attuned to the desert as are the western elephants. During this same period about 200 elephants died in Etosha from anthrax, but it is quite likely that the primary cause might have been malnutrition.

The ecological role that the Kaokoveld elephants play in their environment is considerable, but still little studied. They dig for water in the riverbeds, and during the drought many game animals, birds and insects depended on these waterholes for their survival. Seeds of a number of trees, including acacias, show considerably enhanced germination success after passing through the digestive tract of an elephant. Digestive processes break down the hard outer seed coat, which promotes moisture absorption and results in germination. The elephants eat plants like ink bush and the exotic castor oil, which are unpalatable to other animals. They also open up

23

the dense thickets of tamarisk and acacias of the riverbeds, creating paths and shady resting places which are used by other animals. Furthermore, the remains of broken branches or felled trees lying on the ground often create sheltered nurseries for grass plants which are then protected from grazing or trampling by other animals.

The distribution and status of the Kaokoveld elephants was recently summarised in an important paper by Slang Viljoen. He showed that elephants occurred widely throughout Damaraland and Kaokoland within historical times, and estimated a Kaokoveld population of between 2 500 and 3 500 elephants in about 1880. The Dorsland trekkers, who had left the Transvaal and settled at Humpata in southern Angola, used the Kaokoveld as their annual hunting ground from about 1880 to 1908. Some of their greatest hunters concentrated almost exclusively on elephants. It is estimated that they shot a minimum of 70 elephants per year, accounting for about 2 000 elephants in total.

The calving percentage of these elephants is only 1,8–2,7 per cent per annum (1975–78 figures) and during drought periods there may be no calves at all (though in 1986 the calving percentage was as high as 10 per cent, as a result of good rains). The trekkers were, therefore, taking at least the equivalent of the annual increment of a population of some 3 000–4 000 elephants. It is, however, likely that the population was smaller, and the trekkers were taking far more than the equivalent of the annual calf crop. Consequently, elephant numbers declined. This would appear to have been confirmed by Shortridge with his estimate of 600–1 000 elephants in the Kaokoveld in 1934 (although later events showed this estimate to have been conservative).

Elephants were found throughout the Kaokoveld from the Ugab to the Kunene as recently as 1960. Along the entire eastern boundary of the territory from the Ugab to Ruacana they moved freely to the east. To the west they occurred down the major rivers and on to the Namib plains within the boundaries of what is now the Skeleton Coast Park. There was a wide range of estimates of numbers for these years. Most informed observers put their estimates in the range of 500 to 1 000 elephants at this time. In the light of more recent surveys it would seem that a figure of 600 to 1 000 Kaokoveld elephants in 1960, if not in 1934, was a reasonable estimate.

Our best source of information for the decade 1960–70 is the work of the much quoted Garth Owen-Smith. He estimated a population of between 700 and 800 elephants in 1970. This was made up of about 200 elephants on the eastern sandveld plateau, from 100 to 160 in the Ovahimba highlands, about 40 to 60 in the Heowa valley and the lower Omuhonga River between the Baynes and Zebra mountains, 200–300 in the escarpment and desert region to the west from the Marienfluss to the Ugab, and smaller numbers on the Beesvlakte and in the mountains south of Sesfontein. There were at this time also still some elephants in the upper reaches of the Ugab. It appeared that elephants were not heavily hunted then, and it was mostly crop-raiders and troublesome animals which were shot.

The big decline in elephant numbers in the Kaokoveld came about in the years from 1970 onwards. For the first time in their history, changes in the numbers and range of the Kaokoveld elephants were being recorded soon after they happened. This decline was largely due to heavy poaching of elephants for ivory, much of which found its way into the international trade via Angola. Poaching by local residents, armed by dealers in Angola, was a major source of elephant mortality. Insurgencies in Angola and Namibia promoted the free flow of illegal arms and ammunition which were put to use against the wildlife of the territory. The insurgency brought in the South African Defence Force, members of which were responsible for some elephant killing. Prominent politicians, government officials and others hunted elephants and other game, and elephant numbers declined.

A detailed survey, confined largely to the Kaokoveld north of the Hoanib River, was undertaken by Viljoen from 1975 to 1977. This showed that in 1977 there was a maximum of about 250 elephants in Kaokoland and about the same number in Damaraland. The numbers varied seasonally due to movements to and from Owamboland, Angola and Etosha. Viljoen concluded that the Kaokoland elephants were found in three fairly discrete populations. There was a remnant population of eight cows along the middle Kunene with no bulls anywhere near them. An eastern population of about 250 animals occupied the sandveld as far south and west as the Beesvlakte and the Kowarib Schlucht. The western population of the desert plains and the escarpment mountains numbered 65 animals north of the Hoanib. About 50 elephants were still found in the desert regions of western Damaraland and a further 126 in the east. The total elephant population of the Kaokoveld was, therefore, about 500 animals.

Intensive aerial and ground surveys of the Kaokoveld elephants followed from 1980 to 1983. By the end of this study period Viljoen could account for 357 elephants and 123 carcasses. The population on the middle Kunene was extinct. The western population ranged from the lower Kunene west of the Marienfluss southwards as far as the Huab River. Whereas they had numbered 86 in 1980, they only numbered 70 in 1983. There were six cows on the lower Kunene who occasionally wandered down to the Hoarusib; four elephants between the Hoarusib and Hoanib; a herd of 31 on the Hoanib; a group of five bulls around the Hunkab fountain south of the Hoanib; and 24 elephants in the Wêreldsend area which mainly used the Uniab, Barab and Aub basins north and west of the veterinary fence. These 70 animals are the last of the true desert elephants.

The eastern population of Kaokoveld elephants numbered 207 animals in 1983. They occupied the eastern sandveld from Ombombo Owambo in the north to the upper reaches of the Huab River (to the southeast of the Grootberg) in the south. They did not extend west of the Joubert Mountains. There was considerable movement of elephants from these areas into the Etosha National Park. The highest concentration of 140 elephants occurred in the vicinity of Otuzemba, with about 50 on the Ombonde River (the upper branch of the Hoanib) and on the Beesvlakte. The Otuzemba concentration can be ascribed largely to the far-sighted policies of the local headman, Werimba Rutjani, who has consistently protected the game in his ward, even during the drought when his cattle were dying.

The desert elephants and the eastern elephant population no longer have any direct contact. They are, however, to some extent linked via a central or transitional population of about 80 elephants. These animals occupy a range on both sides of the veterinary fence, in the vicinity of the Grootberg Mountain, the upper reaches of the Huab and as far to the west as Palmwag and Juriesdraai. They tend to move to the northeast towards Omumborombonga during the rains, when they make infrequent contact with the eastern population. During the dry season they move to the southwest and then occasionally make contact with the western or desert elephants. Their movements are, however, restricted by the veterinary fence.

What happened to the Kaokoveld elephants has occurred before in many other countries in Africa, and the process is an ongoing one. Unfortunately there are not always people or organisations around who can set the wheels in motion to stop the wholesale slaughter of wildlife. The Kaokoveld elephants are an asset, not only of the local tribes, but of all the people of Namibia. They are part of the basic resource of a wildlife utilisation industry which could hinge largely on tourism. They can, therefore, earn their keep. Of more importance is the fact that while doing so, they make no negative impact on the habitat — something that pastoral man and his livestock cannot match. In time, when their numbers warrant it, they could also contribute to a viable safari hunting industry, but only when the hunting of these elephants can be sustained.

For the moment Kaokoveld elephant numbers are stable, and the birth of calves in the desert population will soon start the process of recovery. For those of the Damaraland elephants east of the veterinary fence and on the upper Huab, the future is far from certain. They clash with farming interests, and schemes to move them into the desert regions are well intended, but unrealistic. The future of the elephant in Africa is promising only in protected areas — such as the desert regions must become — and only there can they survive. Where they clash with agriculture they will be destroyed. This happened in South Africa and many other countries and conservationists will be hard put to stop the inevitable demise of such animals.

Those in the populated parts of the eastern sandveld will probably also ultimately disappear in the face of growing human populations and the need to maximise conventional and traditional livestock production. It is probably too much to hope that these elephants could also be incorporated into an integrated development and utilisation programme for all the resources of the region. Such projects are being tackled elsewhere in Africa, notably in Zimbabwe. However, the thinking in government circles in Pretoria and Windhoek is still so mired in political issues that it is most unlikely that this kind of forward-looking realism will prevail.

The black rhinoceros is undoubtedly the most critically endangered large mammal in Africa today. It has been hunted to the point of extinction in most countries where it once occurred, and at least 96 per cent of the continental population has been eliminated since 1970.

The rhino is killed for its horn, which is in great demand in the Middle East for the making of dagger handles, and in the Far East as an ingredient of traditional medicines used, in particular, by Chinese. The slaughter of black rhino has reached into the most remote parts of Kaokoland and Damaraland. It was the dramatic decline of this species, as much as

that of the elephants, that was the spur to the conservation action which has been a feature of events in the Kaokoveld in recent years.

The historical record concerning black rhino in the Kaokoveld is sporadic and incidental. Surveys by Shortridge provided the first reasonable summary of rhino distribution and habits in the territory. He found them scattered from the Ugab River to the Kunene, but nowhere east of a line from the Upper Ugab River, past Fransfontein, through Onaiso to the Kunene west of the Ruacana Falls. This range excludes most of the present-day Etosha National Park except for the western area around Otjovasandu, and indeed Shortridge commented that rhino were 'unknown in the Namutoni Game Reserve'.

Shortridge estimated a population of between 40 and 80 animals and mentioned that poaching of rhino by the Himba was already prevalent at that time. He also commented that 'the rhinoceros is the only animal in the Kaokoveld the existence of which is seriously threatened'. He identified the threat as local hunters, who shot them as they approached waterholes, and attributed the survival of a population of rhino to none other than 'a shortage of ammunition amongst the natives'. If the rhino were poached as relentlessly as claimed by Shortridge than it is likely that there were far more in the Kaokoveld than he estimated.

A comprehensive survey carried out by Dr Eugene Joubert of the Directorate of Nature Conservation in 1966 showed that black rhino were more widely distributed than Shortridge had realised. In addition to the range given in 1934, Joubert could add isolated rhino in the Erongo Mountains, a few scattered animals south of the Ugab River and isolated patches of rhino occurrence east of Fransfontein on the upper reaches of the Ugab near Outjo; and within Etosha at Gobaub and Grunewald.

Joubert was able not only to gather information from his field surveys and waterhole counts, but also to compile information on the status of rhino during the previous 20 years.

This was because large areas of the Kaokoveld along the Huab and Ugab Rivers were given out as farms and settled by whites in 1948. Wêreldsend was one such farm, as was Palmwag, and others around Grootberg. On all of these farms rhino were shot by the settlers as part of the ethic of 'taming' the land (and placating nervous shepherds).

After sifting through all his data, Joubert arrived at the conclusion that at the time of Shortridge's surveys there could have been 200–250 black rhino in the Kaokoveld. The decline predicted by Shortridge had occurred and Joubert's estimate for 1966 was that there were only 90 black rhino left. Of these 25 were north of the Hoanib River and 48 occurred in what was at that time (pre-Odendaal Commission) Game Reserve No. 2 – the original Etosha National Park. (There were 8 animals in the east, and the remaining 40 were scattered from Okawao and Otjovasandu southwards in the escarpment country around the upper reaches of the Hoanib, the Uniab and the Koichab as far as Springbokwasser on the Koichab River.) Another 17 were found elsewhere in adjoining territory (Ugab River, Doros Craters, Twyfelfontein). The last-mentioned animals were not only in farming areas where there was little hope of their survival, but had also been reduced to small local populations of widely scattered individuals with little hope of regular contact and breeding.

Within Kaokoland (north of the Hoanib River) the 25 rhino were mostly concentrated in three large areas. These were in the north (Zebra to Baynes Mountains and Kunene); west (around Orupembe and Sanitatas) and in the south (around Purros). There were also a few animals at Kaoko Otavi and in the upper reaches of the Hoarusib around Otjiwero.

The proposals of the infamous Odendaal Commission to cut off the entire western part of Etosha from near Otjovasandu meant that most of the black rhino range identified by Joubert would fall outside protected areas and the survival of the black rhino was therefore in jeopardy. The Directorate of Nature Conservation, under the late Bernabe de la Bat, then launched one of the most far-sighted, successful and significant yet least-known projects ever undertaken to conserve black rhino in Africa. A total of 43 black rhino were captured and translocated to within the boundaries of Etosha (as defined by the Odendaal Commission) between 1967 and 1972 and more followed in later years to bring the total to 52 rhino moved. Had this action not been taken it is very likely that many of these animals would have been shot and Etosha today would not have one of the largest populations of black rhino in Africa.

The bulk of the capture operations were planned and carried out by the game capture team of the D.N.C., led by the late Dr Ian Hofmeyr. Many practical problems relating to drug dosages and the design of darts and needles, bomas, crates and field vehicles, were successfully overcome. These operations and later translocations within Etosha, also conducted by Ian Hofmeyr, ensured the safety of rhino in Etosha and developed for Namibia an excellent rhino capture team.

Rhino were initially moved to the Otjovasandu area and then to Ombika, a waterhole near Okaukuejo, then to Halali and finally to Namutoni. The Hofmeyr and De la Bat legacy lives on, in that the D.N.C. capture team was responsible for catching six black rhino in the Otjovasandu area in 1985 for translocation to the Augrabies Falls National Park in South Africa. Among these animals was an old bull that had been moved by Ian Hofmeyr to Etosha from Damaraland in 1970–72. In 1987 the capture team was in action again when six black rhino were translocated to the Vaalbos National Park, also in South Africa.

Garth Owen-Smith, when he published his report in 1971 on his work in the Kaokoveld from 1968 to 1970, estimated a total population of not less than 100 and possibly as many as 150 black rhino in Kaokoland, north of the Hoanib River. This was a considerably higher estimate than the figure of 25 given by Eugene Joubert in 1966, and the 30 estimated by

Joubert and Peter Mostert in 1975. However, heavy poaching considerably reduced the number of rhino and in 1977 when Slang Viljoen reported on an intensive survey of Kaokoland he concluded that no more than 20 rhino were left. This was after heavy poaching in the early 1970s had taken its toll.

Viljoen also found that individual rhino were seen at localities up to 100 km apart and he argued that if the individuals were not known, it would be quite likely that an overestimate of numbers would result. He reported that rhino had disappeared from virtually all of the localities mentioned by Joubert and Owen-Smith in the Ovahimba highlands and the eastern plateau. There were also no longer any rhino along the Kunene. He reported three individual sightings of rhino in the Heowa Valley, the Steilrand Mountains (Ekoto) and east of the Joubert Mountains (Otuzemba) in 1975. Other than these, the only reports from east of the escarpment were from the Beesvlakte and areas adjoining the Etosha National Park. The rest of the rhino occurred in the western desert areas and the escarpment zone.

To the south of the Hoanib, rhino were scattered in the western plains and in the escarpment zone as far south as the Ugab, with occasional wanderers to the Skeleton Coast. The stronghold for the Damaraland rhino was the upper reaches of the Uniab and its tributaries and the western slopes and foothills of the Grootberg Mountain. The rhino reached their lowest numbers around 1982, when only 50 could be accounted for south of the Hoanib. This figure indicated that most of the previous estimates of black rhino numbers had been too conservative.

Rhino poaching, which was often coupled with elephant poaching, accelerated during the late 1970s and reached a peak of intensity during the 1980–82 drought. By then rhino were being poached in the Uniab Basin and around the Grootberg. The lowest numbers were reached during the dry season of 1981 and the summer of 1982. An intensive aerial census of the western desert region from the

Ugab to the Kunene carried out during July 1982 indicated that there were probably no more than 55 rhino left in the entire area. No rhino were seen in Kaokoland north of the Hoanib, but spoor seen from the air and later checked by ground patrols indicated that perhaps as many as five rhino were left in the western desert regions. Two were in the Nadas/Munutum area west of Orupembe, and three in the lower Hoanib/Tsuxab area. In Damaraland a total of 23 rhino were counted. This count and observations made of known animals indicated a population of about 20 animals in the Grootberg area, and as many as 30 animals in the rest of this range. The grand total for the entire Kaokoveld in 1982 was thus about 55 animals. During these aerial and ground surveys 29 rhino carcasses, most of which had been poached during the preceding three years, were recorded.

From about 1982 the influence of N.W.T.'s anti-poaching surveillance, the impact of Chris Eyre, whom the D.N.C. posted to Khorixas, increased patrolling by Rudi and Blythe Loutit from the Skeleton Coast Park and information provided by Viljoen's study began to be felt. Poaching was slowly brought under control. After the rains of February 1982, conditions for the rhino were presumably also improved — even though the drought had not affected their populaton to any great extent. Reproduction has been good; only two rhino were poached in the five-year period 1982–86, and by the end of that time the estimates of black rhino numbers, based largely on monitoring of individually known and recorded rhino, had climbed to a minimum of 60 animals.

The conservation work in the Kaokoveld was initiated by the S.A. Nature Foundation's sponsorship of Viljoen's study. The information he produced on the decline in wildlife numbers led to the involvement of the Endangered Wildlife Trust and other conservation organisations. Their efforts were then built on by the D.N.C., and the outcome has been an unqualified success. If surveillance and protection can be maintained this population should continue to show healthy recruitment. An identification file listing each of the rhino was kept by Ruth and Duncan Gilchrist and later handed over to Blythe Loutit and Martin Britz. They also measured footprints and noted small features of shape and pattern of the spoor which allowed them and their Damara trackers to identify each animal.

From these records they have compiled a reasonable understanding of the home ranges of the rhino. These are, as could be expected, much larger (up to 750 km^2) than those of rhino in high-rainfall areas like Zululand or Kruger National Park (100 km^2). By keeping records of the animals and regularly patrolling their ranges, they can detect any signs of poachers, which are then immediately followed up by the D.N.C. officers. They also record calving, and when youngsters leave their mothers; from this they will eventually build up a solid body of data on the population dynamics of these rhino.

The desert rhino are regarded as belonging to the nominate subspecies, *Diceros bicornis bicornis*, the original form described from the Cape of Good Hope by Carl Linnaeus in 1758. This opinion is based on measurements of rhino skulls from the Kaokoveld, and the historical record of black rhino distribution. Rhino were distributed continuously from the Cape up the escarpment zone to the Kunene. The original Cape rhino are known today only from records in the literature, and from seven skulls held in various museums. The skulls are considerably larger than those of any other rhino, and the closest in size to them are the black rhino of the Kaokoveld. The desert rhino also appear to be slightly larger than, for example, those from Zululand. They have larger horns and the posterior horn is usually larger, relative to the anterior horn, than it is in the rhino of Zululand or the Zambezi valley.

That these rhino can survive in areas with less than 100 mm mean annual rainfall is amazing. Normally rhino drink every night, yet in the Kaokoveld, because they must move great distances in search of food, they may drink only every third or even fourth night. They utilise a wide range of plants for food, as recorded in Blythe Loutit's field studies over the past few years. In a study carried out in the area of the Doros Craters, in the Ugab valley, it was found that black rhino utilised 74 out of 103 plant species present.

Among the plants taken were several which contain very high levels of soluble tannins, which are normally regarded as a chemical defence mechanism by which plants avoid being eaten. (Others depend upon physical defences, such as spines and thorns.) The rhino were apparently not even deterred by the exceedingly virulent latex and formidable spines of *Euphorbia virosa*, a favourite food plant for them. The milky sap of this plant is so potent that Blythe and her co-workers reported severe skin irritations afflicting the person preparing samples for analysis.

The rhino showed a distinct preference for certain other plants as well, such as *Sterculia africana*, which was often browsed down to a stump by the rhino. Fortunately such plants recovered quickly after rains fell and put out new shoots. The rhino also fed on *Welwitschia mirabilis* plants but sometimes just chewed on the leaves and dropped them. Other plants were fed upon as and when the rhino encountered them, and yet others were avoided.

These rhino are well adapted to life in the desert; they utilise the plants and waterholes efficiently and fit into the scheme of things, unlike man and his livestock which destroy wild places. Their presence adds a dimension of awe and wonder to an environment that is singularly beautiful and that if conserved and utilised sensibly can add immeasurably to the richness of Namibia, and the attractions of its flourishing tourist industry. The Kaokoveld black rhino population is currently one of very few populations in Africa that is on the increase. But this will only last while the current vigilance and anti-poaching effort is maintained.

The Chacma baboon is the most widespread of the primates and is found scattered throughout the Kaokoveld except for the waterless regions. Baboons are more abundant in the wilderness areas and less common where dense human populations occur. Like some of the ungulates of the Kaokoveld, they undertake seasonal movements and their range increases during the wet season. During the dry season they stay closer to permanent waterholes. Like their relative, the Anubis baboon, which occurs along the southern fringes of the Sahara and in the Tibesti mountains, areas that have much in common with the more rugged parts of the Kaokoveld, these baboons are well able to cope with the arid conditions and meagre food sources.

Vervet monkeys, which are more arboreal than baboons, are able to survive only in areas of riverine thicket and trees and close to water. Consequently, vervets have not been recorded except along the upper Kunene and its tributaries east of the Baynes Mountains, and on the upper reaches of the Hoarusib east of the escarpment.

A total of 24 species of carnivores have been recorded from the Kaokoveld. In general, the numbers of the large cats that can kill livestock are much depleted. Scavengers and the smaller cats have survived in apparently viable numbers.

The Cape hunting dog or wild dog is now extinct as a resident breeding species in the Kaokoveld. Garth Owen-Smith encountered small groups in northern Kaokoland in the late 1960s, but during Viljoen's survey no signs of wild dogs were found, and the last breeding record seems to have been of a pack with twenty pups on the plains north of Warmquelle reported in 1970. It is likely that because of the open terrain and the nomadic movements of game, wild dogs in the Kaokoveld occupied very large hunting territories. Their stock-raiding activities resulted in their being regarded as vermin, as elsewhere in Africa, and consequently they were shot whenever encountered. The elimination of stock-raiding predators, including wild dogs, was actively promoted from the mid-1950s through the issue of strychnine poison and service rifles to local headmen by the authorities.

The two hyaena species are still found throughout the Kaokoveld and are able to co-exist, as they have developed very different lifestyles. The spotted hyaena is a social specialist feeder, usually hunting in packs and communicating by characteristic wailing whoops. While the prey of their choice are large mammals like gemsbok, springbok and mountain zebra, they also take smaller mammals like steenbok, klipspringer, rodents and occasionally birds like ostriches. They also scavenge large mammal carcasses.

The brown hyaena, on the other hand, is a solitary scavenger and generalist feeder rather than a social hunter. Brown hyaenas take any carcasses they find as well as hunting small mammals. When times are hard they eat plant material such as the fruits of the narra and tsamma melons. Both hyaena species will take ostrich eggs as an occasional supplement to their diet.

Estimates of their numbers vary, but they appear to be in no immediate danger. Spotted hyaenas are probably the most common of the large predators and are held responsible for more stock losses than any other. They are, therefore, heavily hunted. Brown hyaenas are seldom hunted; their role as pure scavengers, at least in relation to livestock, is recognised by the local people. Spotted hyaenas do not penetrate the desert, except along the rivers, and are not found along the coast. This is the preserve of the brown hyaena, which lives up to its traditional name of *strandjut*, patrolling the beaches and seal colonies for carrion.

The aardwolf, a smaller relative of the hyaenas, is widespread in the Kaokoveld. It feeds mostly on termites of the genus *Trinervitermes*, and in this respect the aardwolf is probably the most highly specialised of the Af-

rican carnivores. It is usually a solitary feeder and, like the hyaenas, is nocturnal. Studies done on this species in the Central Namib indicate some variation in the termite species taken by aardwolves, which can be related to rainfall and habitat conditions: in a dry year a higher intake of the harvester termite (*Hodotermes mossambicus*) was found. A possible indication of the relatively impoverished nature of this environment is the higher proportion of *Trinervitermes* termite soldiers to workers in the diet of Namib aardwolves when compared with aardwolves from higher rainfall areas. Though this could be a result of different defensive strategies among different

termite species, it may well prove that the desert aardwolf is forced to be less choosy than those in areas with more food.

When an aardwolf starts to feed on a column of termite workers (which are palatable) they exude chemical warning signals which summon the soldiers to their defence. The longer the aardwolf feeds on the particular colony, therefore, the more unpalatable soldiers it encounters as the workers scurry to safety. The aardwolf eventually desists and moves off to find another patch of termites elsewhere. In the desert, however, the chances of finding termites elsewhere are more limited and it is thus likely that the aardwolf will feed longer, and ingest more soldiers, than elsewhere. It is known that veldfires and overgrazing result in an increase in abundance of *Trinervitermes* termites. It has been suggested by Slang Viljoen that aardwolf numbers are increasing in the Kaokoveld and that this may be a consequence of overgrazing which may ultimately be to the advantage of the aardwolf.

For the same reason, overgrazing may benefit the bat-eared fox, which is also widespread in the Kaokoveld, although not found along the coast or in the sand dunes. The fox is especially abundant on the intermountain plains such as the Marienfluss, in parts of the Hartmann Valley and on gravel plains such as the Giribes and Otjiha. The Cape fox is more secretive and more strictly nocturnal than either the aardwolf or bat-eared fox. It is plentiful on the plains of the inner Namib and generally less abundant east of the escarpment.

The black-backed jackal occupies much the same environment as the aardwolf and foxes in the Kaokoveld. It is far more abundant and widespread, however, occurring throughout the area. The relative abundance of jackals can be explained largely by their less specialised diet. They take not only insects (as do the foxes and aardwolf) but are also adept scavengers from the kills of larger predators and from natural mortalities. The black-backed jackal is the only one of the medium-sized carnivores to occur along the coast. Here it competes with the brown hyaena for the carcasses of fish, seabirds and seals. Black-backed jackals also hunt small antelope lambs and rodents and will eat reptiles as well. There is, therefore, sufficient separation in food niches between these four similar-sized species to ensure that all can make a living.

Jackals are also regarded as vermin and indiscriminate use of poisoned bait has probably killed large numbers over the years. However, they have maintained their numbers, and they may even be increasing as the larger predators are eliminated. A similar phenomenon has been seen in the Karoo and elsewhere in South Africa.

Honey badgers are not particularly common in the Kaokoveld. They are sporadically distributed to the east of the escarpment mountains, with most records of their occurrence from the eastern sandveld areas of Kaokoland, the Beesvlakte, and from the Ovahimba highlands.

The clawless otter is fairly common in the Kunene River, up to the east of the Epupa Falls. It is not found along the lower Kunene or anywhere else in the region.

The lions of the Kaokoveld were at one time thought to be a subspecies of the African lion and were known in Afrikaans as the *bergleeu*. While they were formerly widespread throughout the Kaokoveld their numbers have been steadily reduced by shooting and poisoning, because of their stock-killing proclivities. They are now found only in the western escarpment and desert areas and in the east adjoining the Etosha National Park. The desert lions also sometimes move down the Hoarusib, Hoanib, Ugab and Munutum rivers to the coast. In recent years lions have occurred sporadically, and possibly only seasonally, on the Skeleton Coast, and have provided some spectacular photographs as well as unusual feeding records. The preferred prey of lions in the Kaokoveld are large animals like gemsbok. There are many recent records of the coastal lions feeding on the carcasses of Cape fur seals, but it has not yet been established whether the lions killed the seals or scavenged the carcasses. Either way, the thought of a terrestrial carnivore making its living off a marine carnivore is somewhat unexpected.

A further unusual aspect of lions feeding on seals is the distances they drag the carcasses. The beach is an exposed and sometimes uncomfortable environment with damp fog, cold, and howling winds whipping up a stinging sandstorm. The lions drag the seal carcasses as much as 2,6 km along the beach to sheltered hummocks or reedbeds. P. A. Bridgeford, who published these observations, reported that the Skeleton Coast lions had also eaten black-backed jackals, porcupines, white-breasted cormorants and Cape cormorants. These lions living along the coast have also used the riverbeds to move back towards the escarpment from time to time.

Lions are incompatible with livestock, and wherever man and his herds have penetrated into the western desert areas the lions have suffered. Several lions were also shot during the drought of the 1980s when they moved eastwards in search of food. Hunger drove them to attack people and dogs, and several more lions were killed on that score. With the improved conditions following the rains from 1982 onwards, people and livestock moved down the Hoanib River from Sesfontein to take advantage of the grazing. Conflict with lions was unavoidable, as the Hoanib is a natural route for lions to take from the coast when moving inland.

A Nama man who encountered two such lions near his goats in the Hoanib valley in 1987 simply shot them. Later investigation showed that these lions came from the Skeleton Coast Park. In time others may take their place, but numbers are now low, and without adequate protection throughout a viable range, it is unlikely that the lion will survive in a Kaokoveld which has been largely stripped of its wildlife resources by hunting, drought and overgrazing.

Cheetah have traditionally been widespread in Namibia, which has the largest cheetah population of any country in Africa. Estimates range from 1 500 to 5 000 animals. In the Kaokoveld, however, they have always been thinly spread. Their numbers declined markedly after 1970 as they were steadily eliminated from the eastern plateau region, and must have fallen further when most of the springbok succumbed to the drought. They no longer occur anywhere in the east of Kaokoland or Damaraland and are only found in the escarpment zone and the inner Namib plains to the west. An isolated group was still present around Ongango, west of the Joubert Mountains, about ten years ago. As is the case with leopards, this animal has in the past been hunted for its skin, as well as being considered a killer of small stock.

The inner Namib plains still support relatively healthy numbers of springbok, steenbok and ostrich, all of which are still recovering from the drought of 1979 to 1981. All of these are hunted by cheetah. The open habitat, with good visibility and a firm substrate underfoot, presents few obstacles to a successful chase for the cheetah, which is a diurnal courser, depending on speed to run down its prey and hunting largely by sight. Because cheetah do not return to their kill after feeding they are not susceptible to poisoning, although they are easily hunted with dogs. Cheetahs are sensitive to competition from the other large predators, but since lions are now scarce in the western desert plains and leopards tend to keep to the more broken country of the escarpment zone, cheetahs will probably survive in this region provided sufficient prey resources are available.

Leopards are widely distributed in the escarpment zone of the Kaokoveld but appear to be absent from the eastern sandveld and the inner Namib plains to the west. They are reportedly more common in the Baynes and Otjihipa Mountains and the well-wooded valleys and ridges of the Ovahimba highlands. They are solitary, secretive animals that can survive as well on the abundant dassie populations, if they must, as on the smaller game animals like antelope and warthog. They also kill calves, sheep and goats on occasion and are therefore hunted, poisoned and trapped. There appears to be an active trade in leopard skins, especially from Kaokoland, but they are not regarded as being in any immediate danger of extinction in the region. Garth Owen-Smith reported in 1970 that incidents involving death or injury between people and leopards, usually hunted or wounded animals, are more frequent than encounters with other animals.

Of the smaller cats, the African wild cat is probably the most common and widely distributed. Being solitary, secretive and usually nocturnal, it is seldom seen, but has been reported from the eastern sandveld and along the rivers to the coast. It is generally not found in the waterless plains of the western regions. As with other populations of African wild cats these have probably hybridised to some extent with domestic cats from the settled areas. Caracal appear to be uncommon, but do occur. There are records of sightings from the lower Hoanib River and from the eastern plateau. They are probably more common on the plateau than elsewhere.

The small carnivores such as genets and several mongoose species are reported from various localities. The slender mongoose is found throughout the Kaokoveld except along the coast. The animals of this region are characteristically dark reddish in colour and quite unlike the fawn coloured form from the eastern parts of southern Africa. This mongoose is easily recognised by its long, slender body with long, black-tipped tail which is flicked vertically up into the air in flight. For some years the Kaokoveld slender mongoose was thought to represent a separate species. Modern taxonomic opinion, however, makes it a subspecies of the widespread eastern form.

The yellow mongoose is a species characteristic of the arid western regions of the subcontinent and is widely distributed in the Kaokoland, Karoo and Namib regions. The sociable banded mongoose, which forages in small parties, has been found along the Kunene River and the dwarf mongoose is more widespread. Suricates are widespread in the inner Namib.

The diversity of antelope species in the Kaokoveld is rather low: only eight are found as permanent residents (nine if the red hartebeest is regarded as a resident). By comparison, the Kruger National Park, which is a quarter the size, has 21 species. The reason for the low species diversity is to be found in the aridity of the area and the consequent limited range of habitat types (which limits the diversity of food resources). Of the nine antelopes, only two can be considered to be largely grazers, namely gemsbok and red hartebeest. The others are either strictly browsers, or else mixed feeders who can survive indefinitely on a browse diet.

The lesser abundance of food in the Kaokoveld environment may also explain why four of the nine are diminutive antelopes (dik-dik, grey duiker, steenbok and klipspringer), two are medium-sized (black-faced impala, springbok) and only three are large antelopes (gemsbok, hartebeest and kudu) — and of these three, hartebeest are only found marginally on the edge of the Kaokoveld and not at all in its characteristic desert areas. Two species which occurred in historical times, eland and possibly roan antelope, are now extinct in the Kaokoveld.

There is a distinct gradation in social organisation and behaviour of the antelopes. Social structure ranges from solitary through to highly gregarious. In general the solitary species and those that live in monogamous pairs or small groups tend to be inhabitants of forest, thicket or bushy environments, while those living in herds tend to occupy savanna, plains and open grasslands. As may be expected from such habitat selection, the solitary forest dwellers are browsers and the open-country antelopes are predominantly grazers. An interesting parallel to this broad generalisation is to be found in the African rhinoceroses. The smaller black rhino is a solitary browser, usually keeping to densely bushed country, while the much larger white rhinoceros is more social and is a grazer.

The solitary or small-group browsing antelopes generally depend upon silence, secretiveness and concealment to avoid predators. The open-country grazing herds depend upon vigilance, mutual warning and flight to avoid predation.

Of the four dwarf antelope species of the Kaokoveld, the grey duiker is the most solitary. Males and females may occupy overlapping ranges but they seldom spend time together. Duiker are commonly active at night. Steenbok are monogamous and the males and females are quite often seen together, sometimes fleeing together when disturbed. Dikdik pairs are seldom far apart, but the strongest bonds are shown by the klipspringer, which lives as monogamously mated pairs within a particular territory.

The distribution of duiker in the Kaokoveld, and the factors responsible for the present distribution pattern, pose something of a mystery. Elsewhere in southern Africa duiker have been able to hold their own in the face of development. In the Kaokoveld, where duiker were only ever found in the highlands from the Joubert Mountains eastwards across the sandveld and northwards around Kaoko Otavi to the Ovahimba highlands and westwards to the Omuhonga River, their range is shrinking. Duiker are also found along the major river courses, which extends their range far to the west.

Steenbok, unlike duikers, are common and widespread throughout Kaokoland and Damaraland, except in the rugged mountains and ridges of the escarpment, although even here, as on the gravel plains, they occupy the watercourses. They do venture onto the plains of the inner Namib in Damaraland and in places are found to within 30 km of the coast as they exploit the riverine and flood plain habitats where major rivers penetrate the

desert. They are quite common east of the escarpment zone throughout the Kaokoveld.

Behaviour, rather than any specialised morphology, allows the steenbok to survive in the inner Namib. Like the other small browsing antelope, steenbok are highly selective in their feeding habits, taking only the most nutritious and succulent parts of their food plants. They seldom, if ever, drink and depend upon the moisture in their food for their water requirements. Furthermore their behaviour, in so far as it relates to activity and rest, is designed to minimise exposure to heat and to maximise water conservation. Thus the steenbok, like most other African ungulates, has a very definite activity regime. Feeding and walking are largely confined to the early morning and late afternoon hours. At these times temperatures are lower or falling and humidity is highest or rising. During the heat of the day the animals rest in the shade of bushes or trees, conserving both water and energy.

The klipspringer is widely distributed in the rocky ridges, outcrops, gorges and canyons of the escarpment zone and in the Ovahimba highlands. They are absent from the eastern sandveld and largely absent from the inner

Namib plains except in the broken country along its eastern edges and on inselbergs. In the western mountains they are not widely dispersed, but are generally more common along major rivers. This is because they are largely dependent upon the riverine vegetation for food, and the rocky gorges for shelter and escape from predators. Away from the rivers there is ample shelter but presumably not sufficient food to maintain klipspringer populations. They are reported to be particularly abundant in the Otjihipa mountains of northern Kaokoland.

Klipspringers occupy a generally open habitat, where they are conspicuous and have many vantage points from which to observe predators. Unlike duiker and steenbok, they are not hiders. Their behaviour therefore includes a very strong element of anti-predator vigilance. They live as a pair, mated for life, and are accompanied by their young for part of the time. They take turns in standing guard, but the male usually spends more time at it. The animal on guard duty generally stands on a high lookout point from where it can see the other members of the group as well as have a commanding view of the surrounding country. The specialised hooves of the klipspringer are ideal for progression over rocks, but sink into sand; the Kaokoveld animals are therefore at a disadvantage when they venture into riverbeds to feed. However, there are few large predators left as leopard, lion and cheetah numbers are low. Klipspringer lambs are taken by black-backed jackals and by black eagles.

To a large degree the klipspringer and dassie or hyrax share the same habitat and — at least in the case of the black eagle and leopard — predators. It is intriguing that the alarm call of a klipspringer, a high-pitched bark, sounds very similar to that of the dassie. There may be more than coincidence in this similarity, as each reacts to the alarm calls of the other.

Dik-dik are plentiful only in the Heowa Valley, south of the Epupa Falls, and surrounding country along the Kunene and in the Steilrand Mountains. Further southwards they are restricted to areas of suitable habitat in the higher rainfall country east of the escarpment zone and along the headwaters of the major rivers. They are not found on the sandveld plateau, nor west of the escarpment. Their distribution, like that of the klipspringer, is discontinuous. Animals are found in isolated patches of suitable habitat which occur around the lower slopes of mountains and in ravines, but not on intervening plains. The ideal habitat is a thicket with a dense understory of shrubs and virtually no grass.

Dik-dik are browsers, feeding on leaves, shoots and plant litter. During feeding the prominent nose is used to scent the food. Ken Tinley remarked, in his pioneering study, that dik-dik in Etosha were most common where kudu were abundant. He ascribed this to the kudu browsing shrubs down to a level at which new shoots and leaves could be reached by dik-dik. Grazing ungulates like zebras also keep the grass down and other large browsers such as elephant and black rhino probably increase the suitability of thicket habitat for dik-dik by their browsing and trampling actions. Along the Kunene the livestock of the Himba have a similar effect on the dik-dik habitat. Dik-dik are normally able to survive without drinking, but use rainwater pools when these are available.

Dik-dik are usually found in pairs, and occasionally in larger temporary groups. The gestation period is about six months and it is therefore possible for a female to have two lambs in one year. Like the klipspringer, the dik-dik makes an alarm call which is described as a high quavering whistle, and the mobile proboscis-like nose helps produce this sound. Like the klipspringer again, the dik-dik has prominent preorbital glands which produce a dark, sticky substance used for marking territory, and uses communal dung heaps.

The black-faced impala is endemic to an area stretching from Otjovasandu on the southeastern corner of Kaokoland to the Mossamedes district of southwestern Angola.

There are none south of the Hoanib River. Most of their number are found just south of the Kunene, in the Ovahimba highlands and southwards in small groups along the eastern edge of the escarpment region. The highest numbers are found in the Epembe area, south of the Zebra Mountains, within the catchment area of the Ondoto River, a north-flowing tributary of the Kunene. Comparisons of recent reports with earlier records indicate that numbers of black-faced impala in Kaokoland have declined, and their range has extended southwards. This is thought to be due to competition with livestock.

However, the black-faced impala, like the black rhino, is one of the species whose prospects have been considerably enhanced by the actions of the Directorate of Nature Conservation. A nucleus population was captured in Kaokoland by a team led by the late Dr Ian Hofmeyr and translocated to Etosha National Park. These animals have increased and are now widespread around Otjovasandu, Okaukuejo and further eastwards.

In appearance they are much like the impala of South Africa, though they are somewhat heavier and have a more pronounced black blaze on the face. They are generally found in small herds, but apparently larger groups are found resting together at night.

Springbok are one of the most widespread of the arid zone antelopes of southern Africa. In the Kaokoveld they are common except in the northern highlands. They are widely distributed throughout Damaraland and occur in small scattered herds on the gravel plains of the Namib throughout the length of the Skeleton Coast Park and southwards. The springbok is probably the most numerous large mammal in the Kaokoveld, with perhaps as many as 10 000 occurring before the 1979–81 drought. Numbers then declined drastically and fewer than 1 000 animals survived. Since 1982, however, their numbers have been increasing steadily, with the largest concentrations being found in the Marienfluss and on the Giribes Flats.

Springbok are well adapted to life under desert conditions, with physiological and other characteristics shared with the gazelles of all the major arid zones of Africa, Arabia and Asia. They can live without regular water, deriving the necessary moisture from their food, but will drink regularly if water is available. They are capable of utilising highly mineralised (salt) water as their kidneys are efficient at excreting highly concentrated urine. Springbok are mixed feeders, eating grass when it is available, and browsing small shrubs and bushes when there is none. They also eat the fruits and pods of various plants.

Like other desert-adapted animals, springbok are highly mobile. Small scattered groups will quickly form large aggregations in areas where rain has fallen and created an abundant supply of green forage. Springbok can breed at any time of the year and the oestrous status of females is apparently governed by their physical condition, so that good conditions can result in breeding. This is particularly evident in the Kaokoveld animals, which breed according to rainfall.

The red hartebeest is not normally regarded as a resident of the Kaokoveld. However, Viljoen reported a few small herds at Omotambo Maowe on the border with Owamboland, in duneveld country reminiscent of the Kalahari. Garth Owen-Smith also reported odd individuals wandering into this area from the Etosha National Park. Their status is vulnerable, if in fact they still occur. No red hartebeest are known to occur in Damaraland.

The gemsbok, like the springbok, is a true desert-adapted animal of open, sparsely vegetated country. They are widely distributed throughout the desert areas of Namibia as well as further east. In the Kaokoveld they are found scattered throughout the Namib plains and into the escarpment mountains. They are not normally found in the highlands other than in isolated populations around Etoto and Orimana. They are also found in the area adjoining the Etosha National Park (Beesvlakte, Ombonde) and southwards in the plateau country of Damaraland. It is likely that gemsbok were more widely distributed in the past but were eliminated by man on the highlands and northern drainage areas. They are still widespread throughout Damaraland, especially between the Uniab and Hoanib rivers.

Gemsbok are predominantly grazers, though like springbok they will also eat fruit, especially tsamma melons, dig for tubers, bulbs or roots, and browse. They have a very efficient renal system and can live without water for long periods. They will, however, drink when water is available and in the Kaokoveld are seldom found further than about 15 km from water. They can also dig waterholes in sandy riverbeds and have been known to enlarge waterholes dug by elephants or Hartmann's zebra. These waterholes are often used later by other animals. Gemsbok behaviour and physiology is well adapted to survival in harsh desert areas. The gemsbok has a very complex system of blood vessels in the nasal area which serve to cool the blood before it enters the brain. They also retire into the shade of even sparse bushes or trees where they lie up during the heat of the day so as to avoid heat stress.

Gemsbok are generally found in small herds or as solitary individuals to maximise foraging efficiency over a large area. However, when rain showers of 20 mm or more fall in an area and the desert blooms, with annual grasses forming a productive pasture, they may congregate in much larger assemblages. As the forage quality deteriorates they drift away into small groups once again.

Kudu are widely distributed from the escarpment zone eastwards in both Kaokoland and Damaraland. Their distribution appears to be limited by available water and they are not, therefore, found far to the west of the escarpment except during the rains. They do, however, range into the northern Namib along rivercourses. They reach their greatest numbers in the north in the Heowa Valley, in the east around Otjitundua and the Beesvlakte and south of the Hoanib around Palmwag and Wêreldsend, and also occur southwards to the Ugab River and Brandberg.

Kudu generally keep to bush-covered hills and gorges, the generally denser mopane woodland and broken terrain. They are gregarious, in small herds. The bulls, however, only consort with cows during the rut. For the rest of the year they keep company with other

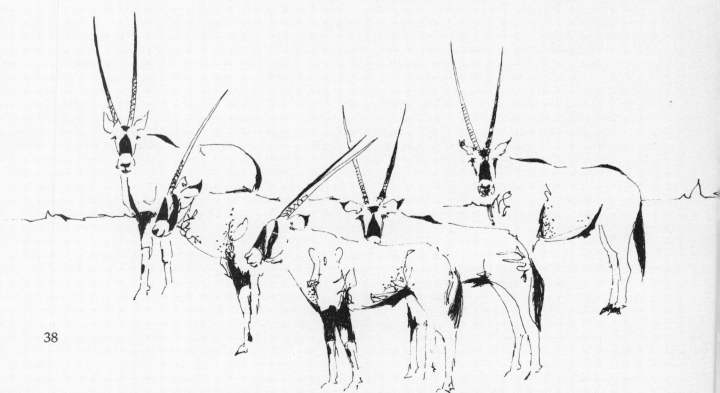

bulls and leave the cows and calves to their own devices. Kudu are alert and wary, and generally stay well within reach of cover. This is especially true in areas where they are hunted. They have a loud, ringing, harsh alarm bark which carries far and is, at times, a regular accompaniment of anyone walking in the broken hill country of Damaraland. They are seasonal breeders, with their calves generally being born in late summer.

Kudu are browsers, taking leaves, twigs, flowers and fruits of a wide range of plant species. They also graze during the early part of the rainy season when new green grass is available.

There appear to be no eland resident in the Kaokoveld, though occasional wanderers from Etosha are reported. There are several historical records of eland in small groups along the southern edge of the Baynes Mountains, but these may refer to nomads, as observers who know the area well have no evidence of their permanent occurrence. There have also been odd reports of wandering animals east of Khorixas, probably originating from farms in the Outjo district.

Warthogs are rare in Kaokoland but common in parts of Damaraland. They are most commonly found in the Beesvlakte area and the sandveld immediately adjoining Etosha National Park around Onaiso and Otjikowares. There are records of them from the Heowa Valley, just south of the Kunene, and they are widespread in Damaraland east of the escarpment zone. They also occur westwards to the Ugab River mouth.

The hippopotamus has in recent times only ever been a rare denizen of the Kunene River. Numbers west of the Ruacana Falls have never been put at higher than twelve animals. In 1975 there were still some at Enyandi and near the Epupa Falls, but by 1977 Slang Viljoen reported that it was unlikely that more than a few individuals were left. Hippo could move down the Kunene from Angola but this be-

comes less likely as time passes, and their numbers upstream are probably also dwindling. Hippo are grazers and they require a large amount of food each night. They are, therefore, at a disadvantage where large numbers of livestock occur and eliminate the grazing, as has happened over large areas of Kaokoland. Furthermore, long stretches of the Kunene pass through rugged country with very steep banks, making it unsuitable for hippo.

Giraffe are today found scattered in discrete localities in the western desert regions of Kaokoland around Orupembe, the Khumib River and as far north as Orumwe; along the lower reaches of the Hoanib, in northern and western Damaraland to as far south as the Uniab River, in the Beesvlakte and Ombonde area, and across the border on various farms in the Outjo district bordering Damaraland. At times giraffe may wander into the Skeleton Coast Park along the lower Hoanib and Khumib Rivers and they have been recorded at Sarusas fountain, 10 km from the coast, but they do not occur permanently in the dunes.

In 1934 Shortridge described the distribution of giraffe in the Kaokoveld as encompassing only the area to the east of a line drawn from Sesfontein to Kaoko Otavi as far north as Ombazu and extending south of the Hoanib to the headwaters of the Huab and Fransfontein in northeastern Damaraland (about 18 km north of present-day Khorixas). His local informants told him that there were no giraffe west of Sesfontein. In the light of deficiencies in some of his reports on the distribution and numbers of elephants and rhino, it is quite possible that his information in respect of giraffe distribution was also not entirely correct.

In 1970 Garth Owen-Smith summarised his observations on Kaokoland and reported that giraffe were widespread west of the escarpment from the upper Marienfluss to Purros. There were still small groups to be found on the eastern plateau between Otjipemba and the Omuhonga River, in the foothills of the

Steilrand Mountains and south of Kaoko Otavi. By 1977, when Slang Viljoen completed his survey, however, giraffe had disappeared from all the eastern localities. The most likely cause of the decline of the giraffe in the east was hunting by local people, who prize the thick hide for making sandals, their standard footwear. They also eat giraffe meat. The only giraffe to survive in Kaokoland, therefore, were those that moved westward into the desert. They are dependent on the vegetation of the river valleys, as the inner Namib plains are fairly barren, though they can probably live indefinitely without drinking.

The distribution of Burchell's zebra changed similarly over the same period, with animals moving westwards as human populations and livestock numbers increased in the east.

There are two kinds of zebra in the Kaokoveld, the plains or Burchell's zebra and Hartmann's mountain zebra. The latter is the more abundant of the two, though it was not always so.

Hartmann's mountain zebra are found in the escarpment zone throughout the Kaokoveld, and on the inner Namib plains (especially in southern Damaraland). They are also found in the Beesvlakte and Ombonde area and from there across the boundary into the western region of Etosha around Otjovasandu. The largest concentrations in the Kaokoveld are found in the Orupembe–Sanitatas area, the Hartmann Valley and Hartmann Mountains, the Giribes–Gonias area and the Marienfluss.

Their distribution has changed over the past half-century, as they have been wiped out to the east of the escarpment zone. South of the Hoanib their numbers were dramatically depleted by the drought of the 1980s, when the veterinary cordon fence prevented them from moving eastwards in search of grazing. They are now found around the Grootberg, Wêreldsend and southwards in suitable broken country to the Ugab Valley up which they are dispersed into eastern Damaraland. In the extreme south of Damaraland they are still fairly numerous in the Erongo Mountains and occur across the Swakop River in the Central Namib. A timely reintroduction of nearly 250 Hartmann's zebra from Otjovasandu to the Wêreldsend area was carried out in 1982 by the D.N.C. The purpose was to assist the recovery of the population from the effects of the drought, and to divert the lions who, with no wild prey, were taking livestock in the adjoining farming areas.

Hartmann's mountain zebra is one of the species likely to move into areas where showers have brought on good grazing, even well into the Namib plains. Large numbers gather in such situations. As the grass withers they move back into the escarpment zone and the aggregations disperse into their component small family groups and bachelor groups. Hartmann's zebra are extremely agile and sure-footed in rugged terrain, and can climb up the steepest slopes in search of grass, or to small fountains and pools. They are more adept than gemsbok or rhino at digging in riverbeds in search of water. Hartmann's zebra feed on coarse grasses, and although they are not ruminants they have an efficient digestive system which can process fibrous grasses.

Burchell's zebra were generally more abundant to the east of the escarpment mountains of Kaokoland, moving westwards as far as the Munutum River and Orupembe in some wet seasons, and then back to the eastern highlands during the dry season. The largest concentration was in the Baynes Mountains until fairly recently. However, no detailed surveys have been carried out since the bad drought of the early 1980s, which virtually wiped out this species. There may still be a few Burchell's zebra in the remote parts of the Ovahimba highlands and in the east. None were seen during the aerial survey of the western regions in 1982. There are no Burchell's zebra south of the Hoanib in Damaraland.

The distribution of Burchell's zebra, like that of the giraffe and Hartmann's zebra, had shifted westwards into increasingly dry country as the competitive pressure of man and his livestock pushed wildlife out of former ranges on the higher rainfall eastern plateau areas. There was, for a time, a greater overlap between the two zebras than had been the case in former years. But the Burchell's zebra cannot survive permanently in the west, as shown by the die-off of the drought, and they are likely to become extinct except possibly in the east.

Among the mammals which are regarded as part of the Kaokoveld fauna are pangolin and aardvark. The pangolin is extremely rare and is found only to the east of the 100 mm rainfall isohyet. The aardvark is not found in the western regions either, but is widespread in the escarpment valleys and the plateau country of the east. Aardvark are also reported to be common along the eastern Kunene River. Like the pangolin, they are specialised feeders, living largely on termites which are dug out of their subterranean nests with powerful claws and then lapped up by a sticky tongue. Porcupines are found throughout the Kaokoveld, penetrating along the major river valleys to within a few kilometres of the coast in places.

The Kaokoveld dassie or hyrax occurs from around the Huab River and Khorixas northwards to the Kunene and beyond into Angola. South of this line the rock hyrax occupies the hyrax habitat of jumbled rocks and boulders, rock outcrops and crags. Both species are widely spread in suitable habitat except in the Namib. They are superficially similar in appearance, but the Kaokoveld hyrax has a patch of yellowish hair masking its dorsal gland and pale, off-white patches at the base of the ears, while the rock hyrax has a patch of black hair masking its dorsal gland and buff coloured patches at the base of the ears. Both species are browsers.

Whereas the hyrax species replace one another from north to south, the two ground squirrel species replace one another from east to west. The Kaokoveld or mountain ground

squirrel is found in the escarpment country and the ground squirrel is found on the plateau country and eastwards. The two are virtually impossible to distinguish in the field, though the Kaokoveld ground squirrel has yellowish incisor teeth and three black bands on the long tail hairs whereas the ground squirrel has white teeth and two black bands on the tail hairs.

The spectrum of small mammals found in the Kaokoveld is wide, including rats, mice, tree rats, hares, springhares, gerbils, bats, shrews and elephant shrews. The distribution of the different species relates to ecological processes and niche separation. Thus some animals are found only in the higher-rainfall

eastern areas, others only in the drier escarpment zone, and yet others are basically eastern forms, like the four-striped field mouse, which penetrate far into the desert by keeping to the river valleys — in the same way as the large mammals and birds exploit the environment.

Wherever there are ecotones (where different habitats meet, such as a rocky inselberg rising out of a gravel plain) there are opportunities for animals to exploit the food and shelter resources of both environments and to compensate for the disadvantages of one by capitalising on the advantages of the other. In the Namib there are many such situations. Furthermore, the effects of the desert climate can be markedly ameliorated for mammals by the coast fogs providing precipitation and influencing food supplies, and by the animals making efficient use of microclimates such as

burrows or protected areas under rocks or plants such as the welwitschia.

No direct studies of these processes have been reported from the Kaokoveld, but intensive work has been done further south in the Central Namib. It is likely that many of the findings of research at Tumasberg (40 km south of Damaraland) will be indicative of situations in the northern Namib as well. They suggest that the small mammal communities

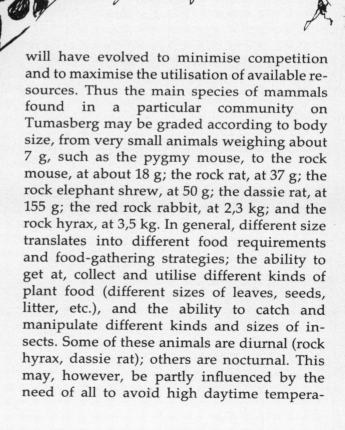

will have evolved to minimise competition and to maximise the utilisation of available resources. Thus the main species of mammals found in a particular community on Tumasberg may be graded according to body size, from very small animals weighing about 7 g, such as the pygmy mouse, to the rock mouse, at about 18 g; the rock rat, at 37 g; the rock elephant shrew, at 50 g; the dassie rat, at 155 g; the red rock rabbit, at 2,3 kg; and the rock hyrax, at 3,5 kg. In general, different size translates into different food requirements and food-gathering strategies; the ability to get at, collect and utilise different kinds of plant food (different sizes of leaves, seeds, litter, etc.), and the ability to catch and manipulate different kinds and sizes of insects. Some of these animals are diurnal (rock hyrax, dassie rat); others are nocturnal. This may, however, be partly influenced by the need of all to avoid high daytime temperatures. Different activity patterns may also be influenced by the need to avoid different predators, such as black eagles and owls. The different animals also avoid competition by occupying different areas and behaving differently. The red rock rabbit, for example, while using rocks for shelter, tends to feed in open areas; the rock mouse is furtive and stealthy, creeping about among the rocks at night; the rock rat is far more aggressive and active; the dassie rat is to some extent social and moves around in groups, while the rock elephant shrew is solitary.

In some situations, as has been shown in the changing distribution of some of the large mammals, species found at a particular locality now may be a recent arrival there. Other species may represent relict populations that occupied isolated inselbergs or mountains at some time in the distant past when rainfall was higher or conditions were different and access to these areas was easy. Conditions may now be such as to preclude any further contact with their kind. Colonisation of inselbergs may now be impossible for some species (which are unlikely to cross the gravel plains) and easy for others. Suffice it to say that the ecology of the small mammals of the Kaokoveld is likely to be a fascinating field for investigation and that from a scientific point of view most of the area is *terra incognita*.

T he reptiles, amphibians, insects and other invertebrates of the Kaokoveld have been little studied. Some groups, such as the frogs and toads, may be represented by no more than 10–15 species. It is possible that there may be undiscovered reptiles in the Namib and in the rugged escarpment mountains. Some of the known species have very small distributional ranges, such as *Angolosaurus skoogi*, a vegetarian, sand-diving lizard which is endemic to the northern Namib in the Kaokoveld and southern Angola. Others are highly specialised for the desert environment, such as the sidewinding adder *(Bitis peringueyi)*,

which moves across the sand by throwing its body sideways into loops. The sidewinder buries itself in the loose sand for protection against the sun, leaving only its eyes exposed to watch for prey. The eyes are situated on top of the head, rather than on the side as in other snakes, an obvious adaptation for its ambush strategy. Among the other more interesting reptiles of the Namib is a translucent pink gecko, *Palmatogecko rangei*, which digs into the sand to escape predators.

The invertebrates of the Central Namib have been well studied, but there has been little investigation of those of the northern Namib or the inland areas. Among the best-known species are some of the tenebrionid beetles, which are 'white' instead of black, as a temperature-regulating mechanism. *Onymacris bicolor* is one these Namib endemics.

A wide array of insect species from various groups have adapted to life in the dunes. There are various beetles, in addition to tenebrionids, together with crickets, wasps, ants and others. There are spiders such as the 'dancing white lady' *(Orchestrella longipes)* (so-called from its habit of escaping predators by folding itself up into a ball and rolling down the side of the dune) which lives in a silk-lined den covered by a trapdoor that collects sand grains which effectively hide it. This spider is nocturnal and preys on the palmatogecko. The spider is in turn preyed on by a black dune wasp which paralyses the spider with its sting, lays eggs on the body of the spider, and then places it in a burrow. The larval wasp, when it emerges, feeds on the living body of the paralysed spider.

The variety of insects and other arthropods and reptiles that live in the Namib desert show many adaptations of form, physiology and behaviour to cope with the problems of living in the desert. Some have mechanisms whereby they can trap and utilise the night-time fog, either by digging small trenches in the sand, as is done by a beetle, *Lepidochora discoidalis*, or by standing on their heads in the fog to allow it to collect and condense on their bodies and then run down to their mouths, as is done by another beetle, *Onymacris unguicularis*. Other animals also drink the condensed fog off their bodies, for example, the sidewinding adder.

On the Namib gravel plains the insect and reptile fauna is less specialised and species can be found which more commonly occur east- wards and elsewhere in the arid regions of southern Africa. The diversity of these lower forms of vertebrate and invertebrate life is little known. Investigation may yet show them to be ecologically far more complex in their adaptations to the arid environment than the mammals.

Birds

The vast, still, arid areas of the Kaokoveld look as though they should be barren and lifeless, yet the Kaokoveld wilderness supports an abundant variety of birds. Many are dependent on the nutrient-rich coastal waters of the cold Benguela current, and many more depend totally on the life-line of the desert rivers, often and accurately described as extended oases. Others survive in the arid savannas and only a few species are totally adapted to a life in the desert.

The avifauna of the Kaokoveld, including resident and migrant species, can conveniently be divided into several distinct ecological groups. In the first place, the seabirds and waders of the seashore fall into a uniform group. They are found only along the Skeleton Coast and at brackish and fresh water pools where the desert rivers end, for example at the Uniab delta. A second group of birds consists of the desert avifauna of the Namib; prominent among these are the larks, which include the most highly adapted desert birds. A third group involves species which are more usually found in higher rainfall areas to the north and east of the Kaokoveld on the Central African Plateau. A fourth group consists of those birds that are found widely distributed throughout the southern African subregion, and the fifth group comprises birds of arid and semi-arid areas of southern Africa, here usually found to the east of the 100 mm rainfall isohyet.

All the main ecological zones of the Kaokoveld support a large number of species of birds and many species occur in more than one ecological zone. In the savanna areas of the escarpment and eastern highlands alone, about 250 species can be expected. A checklist of species for all habitats in the Kaokoveld is given at the end of this book. This list includes 382 species of birds — an indication of how rich and varied the bird life of this area is.

The common seabirds of the Skeleton Coast are petrels, prions and shearwaters, which are mainly found offshore and out to sea. Among these are Cape gannets, while common breeding birds of the coast are the abundant white-breasted cormorants, reed cormorants and Cape cormorants. Gulls of several species, chiefly the kelp gull, occur around the Kunene mouth and along the coast. The Caspian tern is a resident, while others are regular summer migrants, moving south during the northern winter. The Damara tern is a rare species, endemic to the coast of southern Africa, which nests on gravel flats and is particularly vulnerable to disturbance by unrestricted off-road driving along the coast north of Swakopmund. Fortunately there are breeding colonies inside the Skeleton Coast Park which are totally undisturbed.

The conservation staff and visitors to the Skeleton Coast Park have recorded 205 species of birds in the park. These include coastal as well as desert records, in that the park extends 40 km inland. A further 23 species of seabirds have been recorded offshore. Most of these records are of migrants and vagrants.

Among the desert birds of the Kaokoveld are two species which are common throughout the Namib and are regarded as endemic to the area. These are Gray's lark and Rüppell's korhaan. Other true desert birds are Stark's lark, the grey-backed finch-lark, trac-trac chat and the ostrich.

These desert species, which occupy a wider range of habitats in the arid zones of southern Africa, in areas generally receiving less than 250 mm of rainfall per year, possess many morphological, behavioural and physiological adaptations which fit them to this demanding environment. The most obvious of these adaptations is the cryptic colouring of the ground birds. Ornithologists recognise two coloration types in desert birds: specialised cryptic colouring which fits a bird for a particular background colour, such as a red lark on red sand, and generalised cryptic colouring, such as a mottled pattern which fits any background.

Many sedentary desert species closely match the soil colour of their chosen habitat. This, together with their usual habit of not flushing easily, provides them with a measure of protection against predators. This specialised coloration is seen in three larks, one courser and two chats of the Namib. The nomadic species of the arid areas are also cryptically coloured but with a camouflage pattern that matches any dry environment. This is essential for nomadic birds as they move to areas where rain has fallen, and breed there, and their colouring must be adaptable to various backgrounds as determined by particular rocks, soil and vegetation. Birds in this category are Stark's lark and the grey-backed finch-lark.

The coloration of the sociable weaver is also typical of the generalised cryptic type. Although it is largely an arboreal bird, it spends most of its foraging time on the ground, where its coloration serves to protect it from predation.

Most of the nomadic desert birds are seed eaters, to some extent dependent on drinking water. The sedentary species are largely insectivorous and therefore can live independently of drinking water, though they may drink when water is available after rains. Most birds of the arid areas can drink mineralised or saline water and cope with the salt either by excreting it through specialised kidneys or via the salt gland which some birds possess.

The nests of the desert birds tend to be orientated to the southeastern side of a bush, stone or clump of grass. This ensures maximum shading during the hottest hours of the day. Predictably, as this is an adaptation for thermal protection, this nest orientation is less marked in winter breeders than in summer breeders. Most of the desert birds are dependent on rainfall to stimulate breeding activity, but some can breed regularly whether it rains or not.

As many as 107 species of birds have been recorded in areas of the central Namib as vagrants or residents in various habitats. It is likely that slightly more species would be recorded in the desert areas of the Kaokoveld.

A number of the Kaokoveld's birds are found only, or mainly, along the Kunene River. The zoogeographic link between the southwest arid zone and Central Africa is the Okavango–Chobe–Zambezi region, with its mosaic of rivers, swamps, riverine forest and woodlands. The Kunene valley represents a finger-like extension of this biome, which cuts through the Kaokoveld and Namib along the Angola/Namibia boundary.

Birds of the mesic Central African Highlands and eastern areas which occur along the Kunene are the grey-headed bush shrike, woodland kingfisher, Burchell's coucal, little bee-eater and olive bee-eater, the yellow-bellied bulbul, spectacled weaver and swamp boubou, among others.

Most of the common birds of the Kaoko-veld have a wide distribution through the southern African subregion and are well known even to the most casual birdwatchers. These include the Cape bunting, common waxbill, masked weaver, Cape sparrow, fiscal shrike, Cape wagtail, mountain chat, pied crow, laughing dove, Namaqua dove, black-smith plover, helmeted guineafowl, lappet-faced vulture, and several species of ducks and teal which are resident on the larger water bodies and Kunene River.

The birds of the arid savanna include eight species endemic to the Kaokoveld area, and many other species of the southwest arid region and the generally low-rainfall savanna of southern Africa. Typical of this group is the pale-winged starling, which is sometimes found in huge non-breeding flocks of hundreds of birds in the desert rivers like the Hoanib and Uniab, all flashing the pale whitish patches on their wings as they wheel and turn. Also here are the crimson-breasted shrike, the smallest of the birds of prey, the pygmy falcon, red-necked falcon, red-billed francolin, black korhaan, Bradfield's swift and white-throated canary.

The endemic birds of the Kaokoveld and Namib are as exceptional and as interesting to the ornithologist as the desert elephants, black rhino and giraffe are to the mammalogist. Ten species of birds are endemic to a range within the ecological boundaries of the Kaokoveld as we have used the term. This ecological region extends to the mountainous semi-arid escarpment and plateau country which lies along the eastern edge of Kaokoland and Damaraland, stretching as far to the south as the Naukluft mountains and the Central Namib, and extending northwards across the Kunene River into the arid southwestern corner of Angola. These Kaokoveld birds are the Herero chat, Rüppell's parrot, Monteiro's hornbill, Rüppell's korhaan, Gray's lark, Damara rock-runner, white-tailed shrike, Hartlaub's francolin, Carp's black tit and the bare-cheeked babbler.

The Herero chat has the most limited range of the Kaokoveld endemics. It is a small bird, about the size of a robin. Its upper parts are streaked brownish and cinnamon, the crown darker, the tail and rump a rusty cinnamon colour. The breast and belly are buffish white with dark streaks and the bird has a distinctly whitish stripe above the eye. It is generally found among scrubby patches of bush, broken and jumbled clumps of rocks with acacia and commiphora thornbush thickets such as are found at the foot of hills, and around small inselbergs throughout the escarpment country from the Naukluft and Erongo Mountains, through the Damaraland and Kaokoland mountains and as far north as Iona in Angola. It resembles the familiar chat in its habit of flicking its wings in quick bursts of activity. It is generally shy and silent, found solitarily, in pairs or in small nomadic parties. It has a pleasant, warbling song and breeds at the end of summer. The Herero chat feeds on insects, fruits and berries.

Rüppell's parrot is closely related to the brown-headed parrot of the east coast of southern Africa and to Meyer's parrot. The range of Meyer's parrot occupies the intervening area of southern Africa, abutting the range of Rüppell's parrot in northern Namibia and that of the brown-headed parrot in Mozambique and southeastern Zimbabwe. Brown-headed and Meyer's parrots interbreed to produce hybrids in southeastern Zimbabwe, but no hybrids between Rüppell's and Meyer's parrots are known.

Rüppell's parrots are unusual among parrots in that the sexes are differently coloured. The female birds are distinguished from the brown males by a bright blue rump. Both sexes have yellow patches on the shoulders and legs and have blue bellies. Their behaviour, however, is much the same as that of their relatives. They live in pairs or small parties, fly fast and directly with much screeching and calling, and roost and nest in holes in trees. Rüppell's parrots are reported to breed in the dry season when the pods and seeds on which they feed are mature. They also take insect larvae and young shoots. They spend their time in trees but descend to the ground to pick up fallen seeds and to drink. Usually found in the tall trees fringing dry watercourses, these birds are fairly shy and do not perch in prominent positions. They are, therefore, hard to see, but are quite frequently heard.

Monteiro's hornbill is found fairly commonly within its restricted range. It is about the same size as the grey hornbill. Its head and neck are silver grey, streaked with black and white to give it a grizzled appearance. The back and wings are greyish brown but there are conspicuous white spots on the wings; the outer tall feathers are also white. The chin and upper breast are dark while the belly is white. The bill is dark red with a yellowish base. Monteiro's hornbill compares closely in its habits to the other similar-sized hornbills: it forages on the ground, digs for food, eats insects, rodents, fruits and shoots, and hops when on the ground. Its flight is like that of its fellows, with alternating bouts of flapping and gliding. Monteiro's hornbill also nods its head when calling and its call is a *tok tok tok* sound similar to that of the yellow-billed hornbill and very different from the plaintive piping whistle of Bradfield's hornbill, crowned hornbill and grey hornbill. As with the other hornbills, the nesting female is sealed into a hole in a tree or rock face, leaving only a narrow slit through which the male feeds her.

Rüppell's korhaan is sometimes regarded as a subspecies of the Karoo korhaan, with which it shares some similar features. However, Rüppell's korhaan differs in plumage, and occupies a far more arid environment, being common on the sparsely vegetated gravel plains of the Namib and western Damaraland. It is generally a greyish brown to sandy cinnamon colour on the back, with a pale whitish belly. The neck and upper breast are light grey and the face has a complex black and white colour pattern quite different from that of the Karoo korhaan. The two species are about the same size; their calls are, however, clearly distinguishable. Rüppell's korhaan is usually found in pairs or small parties. Their colouring matches their environment and they are sometimes difficult to see unless moving. They run when disturbed or fly with heavy wingbeats like a Kori bustard. Their nest is a scrape in the gravelly soil ringed with small stones in which a single egg is laid. Their duets of harsh croaking calls carry far on the still desert air, and they are often heard long before they are seen.

One of the most perfectly adapted desert birds of the Namib is Gray's lark. It is a small, pale-coloured bird, slightly pinkish gray on the back and white underneath. Its colouring allows it to blend with the pinkish grey gravel plains of the Namib and it is very difficult to spot when it is still. It is usually found in small parties, well spread out and foraging for seeds on the ground. These birds seem to prefer areas around rodent burrows where, possibly, seeds have been dropped by the rodents. They sometimes stand on stones or low shrubs to get off the hot desert floor, and may also shelter in rodent burrows. Like most of the larks they are fairly nomadic.

The diet of Gray's lark consists of seeds and insects, and nestlings are fed on insects only. It derives all its water requirements from its food and does not drink. The nest is a scrape in the ground lined with grass, usually situated next to a grass tuft, low shrub or rock. The incubation period and details of the nestlings are unrecorded, but it is known that the chick leaves the nest well before it can fly. Two subspecies of Gray's lark have been described: a southern one, *Ammomnes grayi grayi*, from the Namib gravel plains between the Kuiseb and Swakop rivers, and *A. g. hoeschi* from the northern Namib west of Orupembe in Kaokoland. This is the subspecies also found across the Kunene in Angola.

The rock-runner superficially resembles the rock-jumper in coloration, posture and habits. It was originally placed in the same family (Sturnidae) and known as the Damara rock-jumper. Later studies, however, showed it to belong among the warblers (Sylviidae) and its common name was changed to avoid confusion. The rock-runner is a small passerine with a darkly mottled grey back, chestnut rump and belly; it has a white chest with black spots and a black tail. The eye is set off by a white eyebrow and black moustachial stripe — two features which it shares with its relatives the grassbird and moustached warbler.

The rock-runner was described from a specimen collected in a typical habitat of jumbled rocks, scrub and grass tufts in the Erongo Mountains. It is rare even in its chosen habitat and is usually found alone or in pairs. It is generally shy and skulking except when singing from the top of a bush or on a large rock at first or last light. It feeds on insects and conceals its nest in the centre of a grass tuft. No details have been recorded on incubation and the nestling has only once been described. It is reported that the chicks leave the nest early and run around like mice. Its chosen habitat is in the escarpment country of northwest Namibia and it does not venture into the Namib.

The white-tailed shrike is a small, pied, short-tailed bird. Its body is mostly grey in colour and it has a black cap, white forehead stripe, white chin, black gorget and black wings with a white patch. The tail is generally conspicuously white. This shrike is found in scrubby savanna and thornbush generally dominated by acacias, but is equally at home in mopane scrub. It can be seen around Ot-jovasandu in the extreme west of the Etosha National Park and in eastern Kaokoland, but is regarded as a common resident wherever it occurs in the Kaokoveld. It undertakes local seasonal movements. The white-tailed shrike is found singly, in pairs or small groups. Its flight is heavy and it forages for insects in trees, gleaning its prey from leaves and bark, on bushes and even from the ground. It breeds during the summer, building its nest in a tree well above the ground. The incubation period and behaviour of nestlings are unrecorded.

Hartlaub's francolin is among the smaller members of its family. The male bird is dark brown and heavily mottled with black and buff on the back. The breast and belly are pale buff with heavy black streaks. The crown is dark, as in most francolins, but the Hartlaub's male has a whitish eyestripe and black fore-head with a russet ear patch. The bill is yellowish and appears disproportionately large for such a small bird. The female is generally paler cinnamon buff with no black streaks on the underparts, and a dark back. The call is recorded as a grating cackle.

Hartlaub's francolin is uncommon. It usually occurs in pairs which occupy a territory of rocky koppies and broken slopes in hilly and mountainous country. They are vocal and call from a prominent vantage point in the early morning. Like other francolins it feeds on seeds, berries, shoots, bulbs, snails and insects. Only one nest is known and it was reported to be a scrape on a ledge. Incubation and chicks have not been recorded. Two subspecies of Hartlaub's francolin have been described. They are *Francolinus hartlaubi bradfieldi* from the Waterberg and *F. h. crypticus* from Onguati in Kaokoland.

The bare-cheeked babbler is so-called because of bare patches of skin under the eye and on the ear coverts. It has a white head, chest and belly with a brownish back and tail and a cinnamon collar and flanks. It shows a conspicuous white rump in flight. Like its relatives it occurs in smallish, noisy, gregarious groups. Their foraging on the ground and in low shrubs and bushes is accompanied by much grating chuckling very like that of the arrow-marked babbler. The chosen habitat of this babbler is thought to be bare rocky ground among thick scrub along dry drainage lines, around rocky wooded hills and open woodland. Along the Huab River in western Damaraland it has been found in tamarisk thickets.

Flocks move around in a loose, straggling group with the individual birds following one another from bush to bush. They often associate with other species of babblers. Little is known about their feeding habits, but it has been recorded that they feed on insects, seeds and fruits. Only two nests are known — they consisted of a loosely built bowl of grass and herb stems placed in a tree. The bare-cheeked babbler is most commonly found in Kaokoland, but its range extends as far east as Tsumeb and north to Humpata in Angola. Though three races have been described, only two are generally recognised. These are *Turdoides gymnogenys kaokensis*, described by Austin Roberts from the Huab River, and *T. g. gymnogenys*, described by Dr Hartlaub from Angola.

The newest addition to the list of the Kaokoveld's endemic birds is Carp's black tit, which was formally recognised as a full species only as recently as 1980. Before then it was regarded as a subspecies of the southern black tit or of the white-winged black tit, which is found from southern Angola across to Malawi. However, by 1980 it had been realised that Carp's tit and the white-winged black tit occurred side by side in the same area and did not interbreed. It was therefore recognised as a full species and named in honour of Bernard Carp who had financed various scientific expeditions, among them an ornithological expedition to Kaokoland in 1951. Carp's black tit occurs in arid woodlands westwards to Etosha and Otavi. It is a smallish, glossy black bird, with extensive areas of white on the wings. It is generally found in pairs and its habits and calls are reported to be similar to those of the southern black tit. It feeds mainly on insects and occasionally also on seeds. Carp's black tit breeds during the summer months; however, the incubation period and nestlings are unrecorded.

As with the babblers, there are several species of tits whose ranges abut or overlap in the Kaokoveld and southern Angola. In addition to the three species listed above, the rufous-bellied tit, the Cape penduline tit, the grey penduline tit and the ashy tit all occur in this zoogeographically complex region of Africa.

The rarity of the Kaokoveld endemic birds is emphasised by even a cursory review of our knowledge of these ten species as reflected in the literature. The incubation period is known for only two — Rüppell's parrot and Monteiro's hornbill. For the other eight species there is little information. The nestlings of the above two species have also been described, as has a large rock-runner chick, but for the rest there is again very little information. The food of most of them is poorly known, and the nests of several are known from only one or two observations.

Two species of birds that are among the rarest in southern Africa are found only along the Kunene River in the Kaokoveld. They are the Cinderella waxbill and the rufous-tailed palm thrush. Both species were recorded for the first time in our region during the Percy Fitzpatrick Institute-Windhoek State Museum Joint Ornithological Expedition of 1965 to the Kaokoveld.

The Cinderella waxbill has so far only been recorded at Ruacana and along the Kunene. It is about the same size as the blue waxbill, but has a blue-grey head, breast, back and wings, with deep crimson rump and flanks. It has a black tail, a black chinspot and a thin black stripe through the eye. Its call has been described as a soft trilling but nothing much is known about what it feeds on, nor is anything known about its reproduction.

In contrast, the rufous-tailed palm thrush is well known, as it is distributed through Angola, Zaire, Congo and Gabon. It is usually found in association with borassus palms or oil palms, in the crowns of which it usually builds its nests. In the absence of suitable palms they have been recorded nesting in baobabs and even on buildings. The rufous-tailed palm thrush is about the size of a robin and as its name implies it has a rufous coloured tail; the wings, back and crown are also rufous and it has a whitish buff belly, greyish breast and yellowish throat. It has a prominent grey eyebrow and black eye-stripe. Its melodious song is heard before dawn and at dark and it is usually found in pairs. It feeds on insects and breeds during the summer.

Several other species of birds also enter the southern African subregion largely within the Kaokoveld biome. They are, however, not endemic and have a wide range elsewhere in Africa. These are the chestnut weaver, violet woodhoopoe, the grey kestrel and the Egyptian vulture.

The grey kestrel was recorded for the first time in southern Africa by the same expedition, led by the late Professor J. M. Winterbottom, that collected the Cinderella waxbill and rufous-tailed palm thrush. Recent sightings of the Egyptian vulture in the Kaokoveld are of particular interest to the Endangered Wildlife Trust, which has sponsored extensive surveys of the former range of this species in southern Africa. It was once virtually limited to the eastern Transkei with scattered sightings elsewhere, but the E.W.T. reluctantly concluded that the Egyptian vulture was now extinct in South Africa. The Kaokoveld records are, however, of vagrant birds. There is no suggestion of a resident population or even regular occurrence of the species in the area.

The violet woodhoopoe has a much wider range in Namibia than the other rare species and it also occurs in the Huila region of Angola. It is sometimes regarded as a race of the red-billed woodhoopoe or conspecific with the violet woodhoopoe of southern

Ethiopia and Kenya. If this southwest arid form of woodhoopoe is shown to be the same as the Kenya form, it would be another zoogeographical case, like the dik-dik, of a species which occupies the southwest arid and northeast arid zones of Africa and is absent from the mesic zone in between. In these moister woodlands, which separate the arid forms by 2 000 km or more, a close relative, the red-billed woodhoopoe, occurs.

The distribution of the chestnut weaver is much the same. The Namibian subspecies, *Ploceus rubiginosus trothae*, named after General Lothar van Trotha, occurs from Rehoboth to the Kaokoveld and into Angola. The nominate subspecies, *P. r. rubiginosus*, is found in East Africa from Ethiopia to Tanzania, including Kenya and the arid northern Karamoja region of Uganda. There are no intermediate populations in the brachystegia woodland which separates the largely acacia-dominated savanna of the two arid zones in the northeast and southwest.

The Kaokoland highlands and the Kunene valley feature prominently as a centre for babblers of the genus *Turdoides*. In addition to the bare-cheeked babbler there are three other species with overlapping ranges in the same area. They are the black-faced babbler, which is widespread in the Kaokoveld; Hartlaub's babbler, which occurs from the Kunene northwards and to the east (thought by some authorities to be the same species as the white-rumped babbler), and the pied babbler, which ranges from Damaraland and Kaokoland eastwards. It is also noteworthy that the other centre of endemism and overlapping ranges of babblers is in the northeast arid zone in Kenya, Somalia and Ethiopia.

An aside to the ornithology of the Kaokoveld is the prominence of a few individuals after whom these rare birds were named, or who played a role in their scientific descriptions. Rüppell's parrot and Rüppell's korhaan were named for Dr W. E. P. S. Rüppell (1794–

1884), who described the chestnut weaver from Ethiopian specimens in 1840. The parrot was named in 1848 by Dr C. Gray, on the basis of a specimen collected on the Swakop River in southern Damaraland. Gray's lark, in turn, was named by J. A. Wahlberg (1810–1856), the Swedish naturalist who was killed by a wounded elephant on the Mababe flats in Botswana, and after whom Wahlberg's eagle is named. He also named Rüppell's korhaan. Hartlaub's francolin was named by Bocage after Dr K. J. G. Hartlaub (1814–1900) the Bremen ornithologist, from a specimen taken at Huila in southern Angola. Hartlaub in turn named the bare-cheeked babbler from specimens obtained by J. J. Monteiro, who collected birds in Angola between 1860 and 1878, and after whom Monteiro's hornbill was named, also by Hartlaub. The rufous-tailed palm thrush was named by Hartlaub on specimens from Gabon.

The Herero chat was one of the last new species of birds to be discovered in southern Africa. It was described in 1930 by R. M. de Schauensee, who is best known for his work on the birds of South America (Colombia) and China. The type is a specimen collected in the Karibib district. He originally placed it in the genus *Bradornis* with the Marico flycatcher, but R. D. Bradfield, a farmer and noted ornithologist resident in South West Africa, realised the error and in 1935 erected the monotypic genus *Namibornis* or 'bird of the Namib' for this chat. Bradfield made many other contributions to ornithology in Namibia and Austin Roberts named Bradfield's swift in his honour in 1926 and Bradfield's hornbill in 1930, the type specimens of both coming from Quickborn farm in the Otjiwarongo district. Roberts had also named a subspecies of Hartlaub's francolin (*F. h. bradfieldi*) from the Waterberg after Bradfield in 1928. Bradfield in turn named a subspecies of Monteiro's hornbill (*Tockus monteiri marjoriae*) in 1935 on a specimen also collected at Quickborn.

The People

The Kaokoveld is only sparsely populated. There are no more than 120 000 people in the region. Yet they represent a bewildering array of ethnic and tribal groups. There are at least eight Herero-speaking groups and about 500 Ovambo in Kaokoland, as well as small numbers of tribal people from southern Angola — the Tjavikwa, Ngambwe, Ngumbi and Kuvare. In Damaraland there are Nama (Khoi or Hottentot) in addition to ethnic Damara or Dama. There may also still be a few full-blooded San or Bushmen in the Kaokoveld.

The welter of tribes has for many years been confused by writers on the Kaokoveld. Recent anthropological investigations have, however, succeeded in unravelling the complex chain of migrations, conquests and acculturations which, over the past century, have resulted in the ethnic picture we see now. Only since about 1920 has there been some stability of tribal and ethnic boundaries, and by the 1970s political and social developments were mixing and merging peoples again. This process will continue and may be accelerated by future political changes in the territory. By the end of the century the picture is likely to be somewhat different from the one we see today.

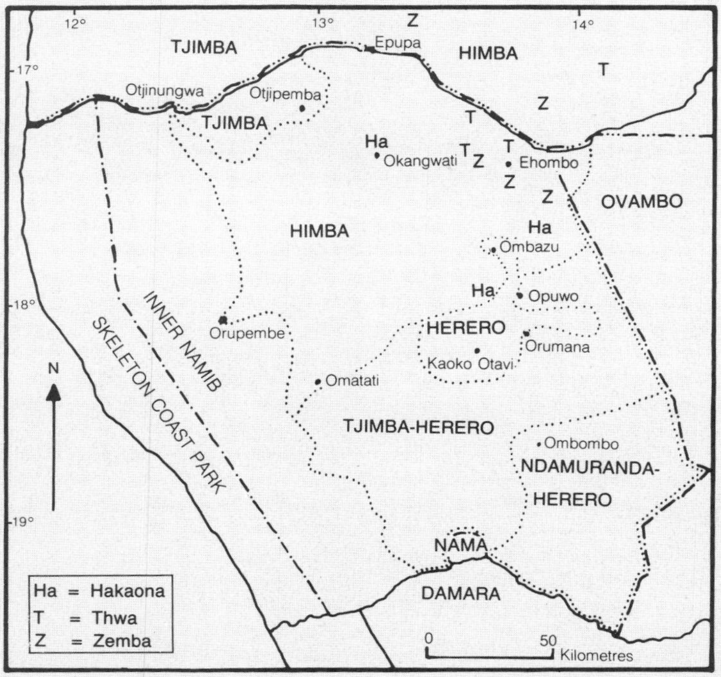
12°
13°
14°
17°
18°
19°
TJIMBA
Epupa
HIMBA
Otjinungwa
Otjipemba
TJIMBA
Ha
Okangwati
Ehombo
OVAMBO
HIMBA
Ombazu
Opuwo
INNER NAMIB
SKELETON COAST PARK
Orupembe
HERERO
Orumana
Kaoko Otavi
N
Omatati
TJIMBA-HERERO
Ombombo
NDAMURANDA-
HERERO
NAMA
DAMARA
Ha = Hakaona
T = Thwa
Z = Zemba
0
50
Kilometres

Ethnic Boundaries

The remains of Stone Age cultures are widely scattered throughout the Kaokoveld and many have been well studied over the past two decades. The archaeological record is fairly good, as the State Museum in Windhoek has supported many research projects into the history and prehistory of the country. Much of this work has been reported in *Cimbebasia*, the Museum's scientific journal. Major archaeological sites have been uncovered at the Messum Crater, the Brandberg, the Erongo Mountains to the southeast of Damaraland, at Twyfelfontein in eastern Damaraland, at the Ugab River mouth on the Skeleton Coast and further up the Ugab in the Zerissene Mountains of western Damaraland, at Ururu close to the Huab River and at Otjinungwa on the banks of the Kunene.

Excavations at the various sites have yielded much evidence of the life styles of the early occupants of this desert world. Thousands of stone implements — hand axes, scrapers, digging stones and hammerstones — have been found as well as organic remains from which much can be deduced. The occupants of the Brandberg sites, for example, moved from the Atlantic coast (as evidenced by shells and fish bones) to the interior. The evidence also suggests that these people were hunter-gatherers and only occupied the sites after rains had brought the Namib gravel plains to life — annual grasslands attracting springbok, gemsbok and mountain zebra that in turn supported the hunters.

Radio-carbon dates show occupation of similar sites as early as 10 000 years ago. Painstaking detective work has traced changing cultures occupying these sites, from hunter-gatherers to pastoral peoples. The clues left behind by these people are many and various and range from the remains of fires to stone tools and plant remains. From the latter, archaeologists can draw conclusions about the diet of the people. The appearance of potsherds less than 2 000 years ago generally indicates a more settled, pastoral way of life. The nomads, on the other hand, had few possessions; being hunter-gatherers they only kept what could be easily carried around with them in their wanderings after changing food sources. The pottery remains are usually found to coincide with the bones of domestic animals — initially only sheep, but later cattle as well, confirming the change to a pastoral economy.

But the ancient people of the Kaokoveld left more than just stone implements and rock shelters behind. They left some of the most exquisite and sensitive art that Africa has yet produced. In a cave on the eastern side of the Brandberg massif is one of the most intriguing rock paintings ever discovered. It is the painting known as 'The White Lady of the Brandberg'. The painting depicts a human figure, with white legs and lower torso, a dark upper torso and arms, and an ochre headdress richly decorated with beads. In the right hand the figure holds a bow and arrows, in the left a cup — or lotus. Around this whitened figure are others, dark and small and everyday. Above the 'White Lady' is a springbok.

Since the discovery of the painting by the German surveyor R. Maack in 1918, it has been the subject of endless speculation as to its origin and significance. It has been suggested that the painting reflects an Egyptian, Phoenician or even a Cretan influence — but there is no supporting evidence for such fanciful hypotheses. About all that is certain is that the figure is not a lady, nor is it meant to be white. Sadly, to protect the painting from vandals it is now locked behind a steel cage. For hundreds of years after it was painted, known only to primitive people, it was safe — only modern idiots threaten its beauty.

The other great gallery of primitive art is the amazing collection of petroglyphs in a secret valley about 56 kilometres north of the Brandberg, known to the Dama as Ui-Ais. Modern whites, with their arrogant penchant for naming places that have borne other people's names for thousands of years, call it Twyfelfontein. There are hundreds of animals and their spoor etched into the flat faces of huge sandstone slabs. There are exquisite black rhino, giraffe, kudu, ostriches, lions and elephants as well as their spoor and symbols. Some of the petroglyphs are more recent and the subjects include cattle.

The site is located in a north-facing valley which opens to a small tributary of the Awahuab, itself an offshoot of the Huab. The valley contains a freshwater spring, and has high ledges from which the occupants could survey the area. The huge slabs of sandstone lie around like the ruins of some colosseum, and the exposed smooth faces of many are like the walls of an art gallery, adorned by the exquisite figures.

The identity of the people who left the treasures of Twyfelfontein and the Brandberg is not certainly known. Evidence from stone implements and tools and human remains indicates that the same people lived at both sites. It has been suggested that they were Khoisan people or Hottentots — not the same as the cattle-keeping Nama, but a different stock from an earlier migration. They are regarded as the forefathers of the Heikom Bushmen and the Namib Bushmen or Strandlopers. They were not small people like the true San or Bushmen of the Kalahari, but tall of stature and

they spoke an archaic form of Nama. These hunter-Hottentots are thought to have moved into Namibia from the northeast, from the region of modern-day Zimbabwe.

The ethnic identity of the earliest people of the Kaokoveld has not yet been established with certainty. However, something of the identity of the occupants of the past few thousand years is known. It has long been held that the people who came first were the San or Bushmen and the Nama or Khoi. Recent research has, however, shown that the Dama have occupied Damaraland continuously for at least 3 000 years — they are at least as old as the San and Nama. By comparison the Bantu peoples are newcomers, the Herero groups arriving as recently as 400 years ago, long after Diego Cao had planted his stone 'Padrao' at Cape Cross.

The Dama, also known as Damara or Bergdama, are a mysterious people whose origins and ethnic relationships are obscure. They have Negroid features, but speak a Khoisan language. They are genetically isolated from their neighbours, the Nama to the south and the Bantu to the north, showing that throughout their long history of contact with the Nama in particular they did not interbreed. Culturally and economically they are an enigma.

Within historical times there were Dama who lived as hunter-gatherers; others were pastoralists and kept goats or cattle; others were traders acting as middlemen between the Herero and Wambo to the north and the Nama to the south. There was also an element of Dama who had a client status with the Nama and herded cattle for them in exchange for food. While some Dama were still using stone implements, others had mastered the art of metallurgy and they were the blacksmiths of their Nama neighbours, who had no tradition of iron working. The Dama were a transitional people who had absorbed the life styles of their neighbours, but had retained their ethnic purity.

At Sesfontein and Warmquelle, which lie on the Hoanib, the border between Damaraland and Kaokoland, a community of Nama, or Hottentots of the Topnaar and Swartbooi tribes, are found. They are the descendants of marauders who moved into the area from 1850 onwards, raiding cattle from the Herero and Dama. The first to arrive were the !omen, or Topnaars, who were the largest group of immigrants. A later, smaller group of //kou-/goan, or Swartboois, joined the Topnaars at Sesfontein. They drove out the Dama and Herero at first, but these people filtered back in time and a fairly stable multi-ethnic community developed around the six perennial fountains, the inhabitants recognising the authority of the hereditary Topnaar chieftain and his council of elders or 'voor-manne'. The Nama kept livestock which they grazed in the surrounding areas, and they also produced crops on land irrigated from the fountains.

At the time of the Nama conquest of Sesfontein there were still San living in the area together with the Damaras. In 1947, when the government ethnologist, Dr N. J. van Warmelo, visited Kaokoland he found a few Bushmen at Sesfontein who called themselves Kubun. His informant, an old man named Khugaob, had temporarily abandoned his hunter-gatherer existence in the Kaokoveld to help with the wheat harvest at Sesfontein. In return for his labour he received food. He said that his people originally came from the Kuiseb near the sea, south of Walvis Bay.

He was born at the mouth of the Uniab, about seven days' walk from Sesfontein. Presumably that meant following the coast northwards to the Hoanib (90 km) and then striking inland up that river to Sesfontein (a further 100 km). However, the distance is only about 130 km as the crow flies. Khugaob and his brother were the last pureblooded San in the Kaokoveld. They both had Dama wives; the only pure San woman of the Uniab group still living in 1947 was married to a Damara man. The San people as an ethnic group in the Kaokoveld were on the final step to extinction. Khugaob's group was the last of the Strand-lopers, finding survival easier around the settlement than on the cold and bleak Skeleton Coast.

Along the Kaokoland coast and further south in the central Namib area are numerous remains of Strandloper dwellings, and evidence of their way of life. These include stone hut sites and graves with associated mussel shell middens, and remains of fish, marine birds such as gannets and Cape cormorants, and Cape fur seals.

At the Ugab River mouth, on the Skeleton Coast, is a unique archaeological treasure trove: an entire village site in which most of the shelters were built from whalebones — mainly the jaws and ribs of baleen whales. The remains of at least 16 whales can be identified at the site. This raises the intriguing question of how the remains of so many whales came to be concentrated at the site and when. Could the bones have been collected over time along the coast and carried to the Ugab? But what a labour it would have been to carry the whalebones who knows how far. It has been surmised that the Ugab people witnessed a stranding of a pod of whales — their building materials delivered on site, as it were. However, the bones have been identified as probably being of southern right whales, which are not considered to be a social species, and it would be most unusual for as many as 16 animals to be together. The most likely explanation, which is supported to some extent by evidence from the shell middens, is that the whalebones were accumulated over time by different occupiers of the Ugab site.

The archaeologists who investigated this unique site dated it at between A.D. 1380 and 1780. It was used well before there was any regular contact with Europeans. A study of the types of bones at the Ugab site shows them to be overwhelmingly from the head and thoracic regions, implying selection by the Strandlopers of the bones which best suited their purposes, and the ability perhaps to dismember entire whale skeletons. The absence of skeletal remains from the limbs and pelvic regions at the site may also suggest that the skeletal bones were transported to the Ugab from other points along the coast where the whales were stranded.

In historical times the dominant people of Kaokoland have been the Herero-speaking Bantu ethnic groups. It is in their language that the name of the land and its greatest river have their origins. It is said that when the Herero moved southwards into the Kaokoveld from their ancestral homelands in Angola in about 1550 the Kunene River was on their right, or to the northwest, so they called the river *okunene*, meaning the right arm. The land to their left they called *okaoko*, from which Kaokoland takes its name.

When they moved towards Ovamboland with their cattle herds they clashed with the resident Wambo or Ovambo, who had migrated southwards before them. The iron spears of the Ovambo were more than a match for the wooden knobkieries of the Herero, who had no iron-working tradition. The Herero then recoiled westwards, entering the highlands of eastern Kaokoland. For two centuries the Herero and their herds lived in this semi-arid, mountainous area until population pressures once again forced them to move. This time they migrated southwards, into the heartland of Namibia. A section of the tribe, however, elected to remain behind in Kaokoland.

Those who stayed on lived the pastoral life, but because of droughts and the seasonally changing availability of grazing and water for their cattle they lived in small dispersed nomadic groups. This system, though ecologically sound, left the small groups of Kaokoland Herero vulnerable to the attacks of the marauding Topnaars and Swartboois from Sesfontein. These buccaneers relieved the Kaokoland Herero of their cattle—and their pride — between 1850 and 1870. For the Herero there was only one option — back to the hunter-gatherer existence of the San, the Dama and the Tjimba, the indigenous people of the Kaokoveld.

The loss of their cattle was a major disaster for the Kaokoland Herero. They lost the central pillar of their culture, religion and economy. The hunter-gatherer way of life that they were now forced into was held to be inferior to that of their proud cattle-keeping brethren who had migrated to the south and had held their own against the Nama. So the Kaokoland Herero came to be called the Tjimba-Herero.

For many years the origin of this name was held to be from *ondjimba-ndjimba*, the Herero name for the aardvark, which, like the seekers after veldkos that these impoverished Herero had become, digs in the ground for its sustenance. There is, however, another more likely explanation. There is a hunter-gathering tribe living in the Baynes Mountains who call themselves Tjimba. The name Tjimba-Herero might therefore indicate the 'hunter-gatherer Herero'. To be able to distinguish between these two hunter-gatherer groups, the conventional usage of names must be Tjimba-Herero for the victims of the Nama, and Tjimba-Tjimba for the indigenous people of the northern Kaokoveld.

In about 1870 a large group of Tjimba-Herero fled north across the Kunene into

Angola to escape Nama raiders. They were dependent on the generosity of the Ngwambwe tribe and forced to beg *himba* — food — and a place to live. For this reason they were called 'the beggars' or ovaHimba.

Times were hard for these Himba but their saviour was in the wings. He was a warlike latterday Shaka named Vita, which means 'war' in the Herero tongue. He was also known as 'Oorlog', the Afrikaans translation of his name, or as Oorlog Tom. He was born in 1863 at Ojimbingwe on the upper reaches of the Swakop River, to a Tswana father and Herero mother, a sister of the Herero patriarch Chief Menassie. Vita's father travelled with the explorer Frederick Green to Angola and the young Vita accompanied them. In Angola Vita met up with the beggars, the Himba, and took command. He organised the Himba into an effective military unit, and throwing in his lot with the Portuguese he went to war on their behalf against various unruly tribes in southern Angola. Vita received arms and ammunition from the Portuguese, and got to keep the cattle which his forces collected from those whom they defeated. In 1906, after the German *Schutztruppe* under General Lothar von Trotha had crushed the southern Herero, several hundred men moved north from the Waterberg and joined Vita. This considerably strengthened Vita's army and resulted in more successes on behalf of his Portuguese patrons, and more cattle to share out among his followers.

After the defeat of Germany in the First World War, Vita decided to move south across the Kunene into Kaokoland. He was now regarded as a great *omuhona* or chief. His people, still known as Himba, though by now no longer beggars, settled throughout northern and eastern Kaokoland. Some of the 'aardvarks', the Tjimba-Herero, were reabsorbed into the Himba from whom they had originally been separated by their impoverishment brought about by the Nama. By and large, however, they retained their name of Tjimba-Herero even though they gradually acquired

cattle and became settled pastoralists once again. Their territory was in the general vicinity of Opuwo and the Ovambo border stretching westwards to the inner Namib plains as far as Purros. Other Herero from the Waterberg and further south also moved into Vita's fiefdom, settling around Kaoko Otavi some time after 1920. The last major gathering-in of the Herero diaspora was the return of the Ndamuranda-Herero, so-called because they had fled from von Trotha's troops into Damaraland. They settled in the southeastern corner of Kaokoland in 1928.

Among the last hunter-gatherers of modern times are the little-known Tjimba-Tjimba. It is not surprising that the rugged fastness of Kaokoland kept a tribe of Stone Age people hidden until as recently as 1964. The Tjimba of the Baynes and Otjihipa Mountains were a people of myth and legend, known to their Himba neighbours but unknown to science. There had been some early reports of mysterious stoneworking hunter-gatherers who lived in the Baynes Mountains in the northern Kaokoveld and the Tjamalindi Mountains north of the Kunene River in Angola. The venerable explorer, hunter and naturalist, Jan Gaerdes of Otjiwarongo, had been on expeditions to the Kaokoveld in 1922/23, shortly after the return of Vita and his people, and again in 1931. His trackers insisted that there was a 'wild' tribe in the mountains who lived by gathering veldkos, trapping, and poisoning waterholes. These people were reported to speak a strange language and to avoid contact with the surrounding peoples. It seemed a myth — a Kaokoveld version of the Yeti of the Himalayas — yet Gaerdes reported catching a glimpse of two of these people in 1922. He reported that they were physically very different to the Himba, being darker in colour, short and stocky.

For decades the legends persisted. The few white government officials who had business in the Kaokoveld and visiting scientists reported the existence of these stone-working people who lived like the Bushmen of the Kalahari. There was even a tantalising report of a kudu carcass which had been found in 1962 near the remains of a camp fire. Pieces of shale, like Stone Age axes and knives, covered in blood, were also found at the site. On the strength of these many reports, the State Museum in Windhoek mounted an expedition to the Baynes Mountains in September 1964. The expedition found two bands of people, calling themselves ovaTjimba, who differed physically from other Herero peoples of the area, and who were still making and using stone implements and following a hunter-gatherer way of life. All this in 1964, when the American Apollo space programme was reaching for the moon and Sputnik was history.

The expedition met their first group of stone-working people at Okombambi, in the foothills of the Baynes Mountains 24 km south of the Kunene. The group consisted of three men, six women and five children. They were, as had been reported, much darker than the Himba, of short and stocky build with small hands and feet, and with facial features more Negroid in character than the Hamitic look of the Himba and other Herero peoples. At Otjinungwa, to the west of the Marienfluss, the expedition found another small group of ova-Tjimba. This group consisted of only one man, named Kaupatana Tjambiru, his wife and small son and his mother-in-law. Both groups of Tjimba were living temporarily with other people: the Okombambi group explained that they had come down from the mountains because of drought and they brought with them a sick child for whom they sought medicine. Kaupatana's group had also left their mountain home because of drought and were living around a cattle control post on the international border along the Kunene. Kaupatana was an expert in making stone implements, including scrapers and knives which he used in his daily hunting life.

The Tjimba roamed through the mountains, going where the game went, or where a shower of rain had created the right growth conditions for the roots, berries and fruits which their womenfolk gathered. The men hunted and collected honey. They had no permanent homes, moving as the environment demanded of them. They made fire by twirling a soft firestick in a harder one, they used arrows poisoned with the sap of *Adenium bohmianum* for killing large game, and snared small mammals like hares, and birds such as guineafowl and francolin. They used no cooking utensils, preparing their food in the embers or cooking on heated rocks; they transported water in bark containers, and lived without cattle or goats, religion or music, political structures or chiefs. Each band was independent and lived its own life, almost exactly like the people of the Brandberg thousands of years ago.

Subsequent expeditions contacted Kaupatana and his kinsmen and studied them anthropologically. On the evidence of measured physical features and the patterns of their fingerprints, it was found that the Tjimba were indeed a very different ethnic group from the Himba. They were closely related to the iron-working Thwa of eastern Kaokoland, who like the Tjimba are a Negroid pre-Bantu people who lived here before the Bantu invasions of the sixteenth century. They were not related to the Damara or Khoisan peoples.

In 1974 it was estimated that there were fewer than 150 Tjimba left. However, even in the sixties, when they were first made known to science, the ancient way of life was breaking down. They had started using metal arrowheads and knives; they were living in closer contact with Himba, for whom they acted as herdsmen in exchange for food; they were adopting the Herero culture and dress, and their own language was forgotten. The old ways were dying, and the skills which had sustained them in their hunter-gatherer existence were of less use as they became more settled. In 1970 Kaupatana died, and with his passing one of the last links to the Stone Age was broken.

Other ethnic groups who settled in Kaokoland included the Zemba, Hakaona and the Thwa. These people originally came to Kaokoland from Angola as specialists and diviners, in the case of the closely related Zemba and Hakaona, and as ironsmiths, in the case of the Thwa. They have largely adopted Herero culture, language and dress and many no longer practise their ancestral professions. The Thwa are darker, short-statured, Negroid people who show none of the Hamitic features of the Herero. They settled among the Herero and provided their specialist services in exchange for cattle and food.

These three ethnic groups are small — in 1974 there were no more than about 500 Zemba and Hakaona, and only about 250 Thwa. About 100 Angolan tribesmen from the Tjavikwa, Ngumbi and Kuvare tribes have also settled in the area, while hundreds of Ovambo are employed in the government service at Opuwo and at the Ruacana hydro-electric scheme on the Kunene.

Conservation, tourism and the future

The year 1970 is a convenient one for beginning a chronicle of the recent conservation history of the Kaokoveld. In that year the recommendations of the Odendaal Commission were implemented. The Commission had been appointed in 1962 by the South African government to look into means of realising the policy of separate political development of ethnic groups in South West Africa. Among the recommendations of the Commission was the establishment of two national homelands, Kaokoland and Damaraland. Their creation required the ceding of nearly 16 000 square kilometres of the Etosha Game Reserve (at the time, part of Game Reserve No. 2 of the German colonial era, created in 1907). Most of this land was absorbed into Damaraland or the newly created Skeleton Coast Park. Kaokoland also largely lost the status of game reserve which it had acquired in 1928. Since that time it had been both a tribal reserve for the descendants of Chiefs Oorlog, Muhona Katiti and Kusupi and a game reserve falling into the old Game Reserve No. 2.

The old order changed rapidly from then onwards. Whereas the area from the Ugab to Hoanib rivers and inland to Otjovasandu had been a game reserve, it now had no specific legal protection and the Directorate of Nature Conservation in Windhoek no longer had any jurisdiction over the area. Furthermore, development was accelerated through the creation of new homeland government infrastructures. This resulted in rapid development of roads, boreholes, cattle marketing and veterinary services, health services, township development and education, but no parallel development in the wildlife conservation field. The two new homeland governments were served by a single nature conservation officer who was based in Windhoek but reported to Pretoria. The completion of the Ruacana hydro-electric scheme on the Kunene River had an inevitable impact on the regional economy and lifestyle. The balanced co-existence of pastoral man with nomadic wildlife was to be gradually, but irredeemably, disrupted.

Up until the 1970s there was no excessive hunting in Kaokoland — the people, by and large, lived off their livestock and looked down on hunting as a way of life. Predators that were a threat to their flocks and herds were hunted or poisoned, black rhino and giraffe were occasionally shot. The drastic decline of game numbers, and the imminent demise of black rhino foreseen by Shortridge had not transpired.

Conservationists saw the deproclamation of much of Etosha as a tragedy. In view of the unsuitability of the land for permanent settlement, and the degradation foreseen, this action was widely deplored. The D.N.C. under Bernabe de la Bat had done all that they could to avert the loss of the area from Etosha. Their efforts over many years were stymied. Fortunately, however, they went ahead with the translocation of black rhino and black-faced impala to the remaining protected section of Etosha.

The first public alarm concerning events in Kaokoland was sounded by Garth Owen-Smith, who was agricultural officer for the territory from 1968 to 1970. He published a report on the state of wildlife in the territory, in 1971. This was followed by a paper which he presented at a meeting of the South African Association for the Advancement of Science in Durban in July 1971. This paper was published in the *South African Journal of Science* in February 1972. Owen-Smith gave his personal recommendations for realistic land use in the Kaokoveld, based on fundamental ecological principles, the recognition of the place of wildlife as the primary renewable natural resource of the region and the needs of the human inhabitants of Kaokoland.

The Wildlife Society of South Africa commissioned a report from Ken Tinley which contained alternative proposals for a division of land between man and wildlife. The government was not to be swayed. The responsible Minister issued a statement committing the government to the development of appropriate game reserves and the conservation of the

fauna and flora, but took no action. He did, however, appoint Professor Fritz Eloff in April 1974 to prepare a master plan for the conservation, management and utilisation of nature reserves in Damaraland and Kaokoland.

Professor Eloff and his colleagues undertook five extensive surveys of the area and interviewed numerous people with local and specialised knowledge. They issued four interim reports before their final comprehensive reports appeared in August 1977. The first interim report, submitted late in 1974, dealt with the alignment of the veterinary cordon fence in northern Damaraland. This issue had already been raised by D.N.C. officials behind the scenes, as they had no jurisdiction over the area. They asked that areas west of the 100 mm isohyet be included in a proposed game reserve and not be allocated for farming. These proposals would have ensured a viable dry-season concentration area for game from the western inner Namib and escarpment. The proposals were ignored and the veterinary fence was erected too far to the west. Consequently hundreds of animals died on the fence in the drought of the late 1970s as they tried to follow their traditional movements to the east.

As illegal hunting and trade in skins, rhino horn and ivory were rapidly taking on alarming proportions, a second interim report was submitted in February 1975. This report urged the government to proclaim protected areas in Kaokoland and Damaraland as a matter of urgency, to appoint conservation officers, to promote research into the ecology of the area and to decide on a tourism policy. It also suggested that the co-operation of the Directorate of Nature Conservation be sought. This report focused attention in particular on the rapidly declining elephant and black rhino populations. Again no action was taken. By June 1976 the final boundaries for a game reserve in Kaokoland were suggested by Professor Eloff and his committee. This included all of the Namib, inner Namib and escarpment country west of the 150 mm rainfall isohyet, including the Baynes and Otjihipa mountains. The proposals were based on sound ecological and land-use principles and included specific proposals for the welfare of the people who had moved into the western desert areas. No action was taken.

The final interim report dealing with the boundaries of the proposed game reserve for Damaraland was issued in November 1976. The proposals were that all the territory to the west of the 100 mm rainfall isohyet be used exclusively for wildlife and that the veterinary fence which had been erected along a line that guaranteed conflict with wildlife migrations, cutting animals off from waterholes and dry season refuges, be realigned as had been suggested two years earlier. The proposals were largely ignored. The final master plan for Kaokoland was submitted in August 1977, with the Damaraland plan following in December 1977.

The master plans drawn up by Professor Eloff and his committee were never publicised, nor were they implemented. Had they been implemented then it is certain that today there would have been viable game reserves with a flourishing wildlife industry based on tourism and safari hunting. Instead, most of the opportunities were lost.

While the Eloff investigation was going on, other voices were agitating for action to be taken. The Southern African Nature Foundation (S.A.N.F.) in particular was alarmed by developments in the region. The S.A.N.F. sponsored a broad ecological survey of Kaokoland from 1975 to 1977, which was undertaken by Slang Viljoen. Much basic information on Kaokoland was obtained and a comprehensive stocktaking of large mammal populations was achieved. The value of Viljoen's work, for which he received his M.Sc. degree in 1980 from the University of Pretoria, is clearly reflected in this book. It was a landmark study and a valuable reference for decision making. Professor Eloff and his colleagues also relied on Viljoen's work. The co-operation was further enhanced in that Vil-

joen's academic supervisors were Professors Bothma and Theron, who themselves were members of Eloff's team.

In 1975 the President of the S.A.N.F., Dr Anton Rupert, revealed that the Prime Minister of South Africa, Mr B. J. Vorster, had given an undertaking that the largest nature conservation area in the world was to be proclaimed in Namibia. This included the areas which would be proposed by Professor Eloff for Kaokoland and Damaraland nature reserves linked to Etosha. An announcement was published in *African Wildlife* in February 1976, together with three evocative Kaokoland photographs. Dr Rupert was quoted as saying: 'A contiguous nature conservation area covering 72 000 square kilometres is being planned for the northern part of South West Africa. This allays many fears which scientists of the International Union for the Conservation of Nature and Natural Resources and the World Wildlife Fund have had, as regards the future of this important habitat. This conservation area will include the existing Etosha Game Reserve as well as the Skeleton Coast Park and will be more than three times the size of the Kruger National Park and indeed one of the largest in the world.'

Dr Rupert also said that the creation of the area would be 'one of the most important events in the history of nature conservation', and indeed it would have been had anything come of it. Sadly, no further details of the proposals were ever published, no maps appeared, and nothing ever came of the announcement.

While Dr Rupert, in good faith, made his announcement the situation on the ground was deteriorating rapidly. Illegal hunting of, in particular, elephant, black rhino and black-faced impala was becoming epidemic. In April 1974, when anti-Portuguese insurgency in Angola ended with the coup in Lisbon, bands of guerrillas became the authorities overnight. Hunting of elephants and rhino in southern Angola accelerated and was carried over into Kaokoland. Arms and ammunition were easily obtained in Angola. The political changes in

Angola gave SWAPO insurgents a new lease of life with freedom of movement, abundant supplies and renewed offensives and the opening of a western front in Kaokoland. The S.A. Defence Force invaded Angola in 1975, in support of UNITA at the outbreak of civil war in that country when the Portuguese departed. There was insurrection and chaos. Between 2 000 and 3 000 military magazine rifles and 200 000 rounds of ammunition were issued to selected residents of Kaokoland, to protect themselves against SWAPO insurgents — but there was nothing to prevent these weapons being used against game. At the same time the price of ivory and rhino horn was climbing and the demand increasing. All the complex events of the mid-seventies were seemingly channelled by a malignant fate to work against the survival of wildlife in the Kaokoveld.

The final act in the unfolding destruction of the wildlife of the Kaokoveld was played out from about 1977 to 1981. This was the worst drought on record. Wildlife and livestock died in their thousands, except for elephants, rhino and giraffe, which could cope easily with the drought conditions. Many of the people also lost their cattle — their very livelihood — and turned to hunting as a means of subsistence. The income from ivory and rhino horn could help to replace their ravaged herds. The intensity of hunting increased and it seemed likely that the final stage leading to the extinction of the elephants and rhino would soon be reached.

In July 1977 a press investigation focused on some of the illegal hunting which had been taking place in Kaokoland. This was followed in 1978 by a report from Clive Walker to the International Union for the Conservation of Nature and Natural Resources (I.U.C.N.), the S.A. government and the S.A.D.F. This report drew the attention of the authorities to the rapidly deteriorating state of affairs. By June 1979 the S.A. Nature Foundation had agreed to launch an urgent study of the rhino and elephant situation in the Kaokoveld. This work was also to be done by Slang Viljoen. The

project was formally launched at a dinner in Windhoek, sponsored by Mr Ernst Taeuber, a trustee of the S.A.N.F., which was arranged to call attention to the situation. The Endangered Wildlife Trust also pledged its support and agreed to sponsor a number of aerial surveys, starting in 1980.

The surveys found large numbers of rhino and elephant carcasses, and showed that poaching extended well into western Damaraland. By 1980 the black rhino had been virtually wiped out in Kaokoland and only a few elephants were left. The Endangered Wildlife Trust was now in the forefront of the media campaign to arouse the authorities to action. The I.U.C.N. African Elephant and Rhino Specialist Group announced at a meeting in Zimbabwe that the Kaokoveld elephant and rhino were one of the most important populations in Africa, and urged their protection.

The political climate in Namibia was also changing at this time, and the rigid insistence on separate governments for the two territories was being relaxed. The Administrator-General started a movement towards normalising affairs. The Directorate of Nature Conservation, for years prevented from taking effective action in territories which were ostensibly governed directly from Pretoria, was able to appoint Chris Eyre as its first Nature Conservation Officer for Damaraland in 1980. In later years more appointments were to follow in Kaokoland, and slowly a semblance of order was to be enforced upon the wildlife scene.

At the same time, the initiatives from outside of the government, largely led by Blythe Loutit and Ina Britz, had resulted in the formation of the Namibia Wildlife Trust (N.W.T.) in 1982. The N.W.T. was modelled on the Endangered Wildlife Trust and received strong support from Clive Walker and his colleagues. The priority action for the N.W.T. was to assist the Directorate of Nature Conservation in its initial efforts to stop poaching and to promote the conservation of the elephants and black rhino of the Kaokoveld. Garth

64

Owen-Smith, a ranger in Etosha at the time, resigned his post to head the N.W.T.'s Damaraland/Kaokoland Desert Project. He and Karl Peter Erb were stationed at Wêreldsend, the exploration camp belonging to Consolidated Diamond Mines. Vehicles and operating funds were provided by the Endangered Wildlife Trust, the People's Trust for Endangered Species of the United Kingdom, the Foundation to Save African Endangered Wildlife of New York, the Wildlife Society of South West Africa, mining and business houses and many concerned private individuals.

Chris Eyre and Garth Owen-Smith worked together extremely well. They soon realised that the local people would have to be involved in conservation action if it was to have any hope of success in the long term. They committed a great deal of time and effort towards converting the traditional leaders of the territories to their cause. They succeeded and the tribal authorities banned hunting. This was a major achievement. By mid-1983 the work of Chris and Garth had created a climate in which it was possible to launch what was to become known as the auxiliary game guard system. The tribal headmen appointed game guards whose duty it was to patrol their areas and to report poaching. The information was then passed on to the Directorate of Nature Conservation, whose officers alone were legally empowered to take action. Because the D.N.C. had neither the manpower nor the money to adequately patrol the entire Kaokoveld the auxiliary game guard system was invaluable in extending the D.N.C.'s eyes and ears. The system worked well and by late 1982 poaching had been brought under control, with detection and legal action the certain fate of poachers.

The Directorate of Nature Conservation accepted full responsibility for the conservation of wildlife in Kaokoland and Damaraland by the end of 1984. By the end of that year much of the activity of the Endangered Wildlife Trust and the Namibia Wildlife Trust had been phased out as the D.N.C. gradually strengthened its grip. The Endangered Wildlife Trust, however, still supports the auxiliary game guard system financially. Blythe Loutit, with the support of various sponsors, also still maintains an interest in the rhino situation. A repeat of the events of the 1970s is most unlikely and the future is more promising than it has been for many years.

The extensive publicity the Kaokoveld has generated in recent years has fired the imagination of would-be visitors in search of African desert-dwelling wildlife, especially the rhino and elephant. This is understandable, but unfortunately it brings with it problems in the form of pollution, off-road driving, disturbance of wildlife and general disruption of the fragile ecosystem of the wilderness.

Tourism is recognised for its potential as a revenue earner, promoting employment and

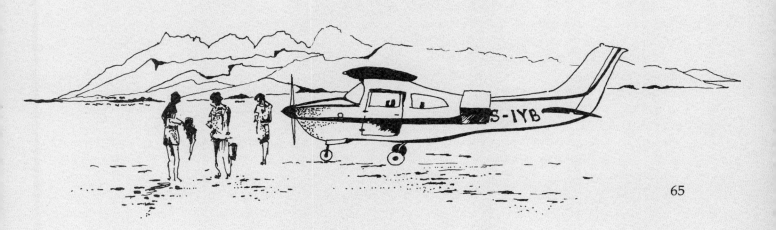

development. Tourism featured largely in the proposals of all who have made plans for the territory, including Professor Eloff and his colleagues, Garth Owen-Smith and Ken Tinley. However, not all aspects of tourism are desirable, and the future of tourism in the Kaokoveld will have to be strictly controlled by the authorities. The Kaokoveld should not be open to all on a do-it-yourself basis, as it is at present.

The intricate ecosystems of the Namib desert are particularly vulnerable to human disturbance and very different from savanna and woodland regions with higher rainfall. This has already been recognised by the Directorate of Nature Conservation, which has not only placed restrictions on access to the areas under its control, but has also made an effort to educate visitors to the damage they can cause. Off-road driving is particularly easy on the wide gravel plains, and people seem to be exhilarated by being able to travel through wild country unfettered by roads. Yet vehicle tracks in the desert damage plants, destroy lichens and the complex insect communities which they support; the camouflaged nests, eggs and nestlings of ground-nesting birds are difficult to see and are easily crushed (this is a particular threat to the Damara tern); compaction of the gravel by vehicles inhibits seed germination, and vehicle tracks remain conspicuous for years, a permanent scar on the face of the land.

The increasing impact of tourists travelling and camping in the Kaokoveld is clear to see in the riverbed systems far from the coast. Because travel is easiest along the riverbeds most visitors use them as roads. The riverbeds are also the main feeding areas of many of the large mammals, consequently disturbance is greatest in the optimum habitat for rhino, elephant and giraffe. Disturbance of wildlife has worried conservationists for years, particularly as rhino and elephant often travel great distances between waterholes, only to arrive and be confronted by campers who chase them away, their thirst unslaked.

Animals are also frequently disturbed by over-eager photographers, which places an unnecessary stress on them.

Litter and its disposal is a major problem. The remains of campfires and garbage desecrate many a quiet spot in the wilderness. The use of firewood is a further problem. In an environment such as the Kaokoveld, firewood is not abundant. Temperatures can plunge dramatically at night, resulting in over-use of this resource. Apart from the value of firewood to the local people, whose tradition requires them to keep a sacred fire burning in each village, the biological role of litter, of which dry wood is a part, is of great importance.

Apart from an excellent rest camp at Khorixas, a safari camp at Palmwag and accommodation provided by the Directorate of Nature Conservation at Terrace Bay on the Skeleton Coast, there is no permanent accommodation for visitors in the Kaokoveld.

The regulation of visitor traffic to the area, and the logic of extracting a fee from visitors which can be ploughed back into the services required to protect the Kaokoveld is now a major issue. The best hope is that some form of national park or game reserve will be proclaimed with the same status as Etosha or the Namib/Naukluft National Park. The Directorate of Nature Conservation has more than proved itself to be a competent authority which could control the area and develop a few selected rest camps and tourist routes with all necessary safeguards for the environment and the wildlife. The Kaokoveld wildlife tourist industry could easily and logically be integrated into the D.N.C.'s Etosha operations via the planned rest camp at Otjovasandu.

The regional authorities of Kaokoland and Damaraland could also derive benefits from allowing the D.N.C. to handle tourism matters. Apart from employment and services which would be advantageous to local people, the authorities could also receive a substantial revenue once the area is properly functioning. Only then will there be a certain guarantee that the survival of the rhino and elephant will be assured for the future, and that the fragile wilderness will endure.

Epilogue: The Directorate of Nature Conservation, with its manpower and budget already stretched to the limit, will be required to commit even more resouces to anti-poaching operations in Etosha and in the Kaokoveld. The non-governmental organisations still have a role to play, in concert with the government. The auxiliary game guards still function under the control of the D.N.C. staff, but they are financially supported by the Endangered Wildlife Trust. Blythe Loutit still monitors the rhino situation from her new base at Khorixas, where Rudi Loutit is now the Chief Nature Conservation Officer for Damaraland and the Skeleton Coast Park. Her patrols are expensive and will require continued support, as will the other elements of the integrated Damara/Kaokoland project of the D.N.C.

The D.N.C., now clearly in control of the area, has welcomed the commitment of non-governmental organisations, within clearly defined limits, to assisting the conservation effort in the Kaokoveld. The Director, Mr Polla Swart, serves on the board of the recently created S.W.A./Namibia Nature Foundation. It is through the S.W.A./N.N.F. that the Rhino and Elephant Foundation will work to make its own contribution to research, conservation and monitoring projects in the future.

There are still many problems and difficulties to be overcome, but unlike the situation a decade ago, the problems are recognised and a framework for recovery has been established. The conservation authorities of the Transitional Government are in the lead. The achievement of independence for South West Africa/Namibia is the stated objective not only of the majority of the people of the territory, but also of the South African government. The independence of Namibia is likely to result in the strengthening of central government authority in Windhoek, and a tightening of control. The D.N.C. will

probably be in a stronger position then to deal with conservation matters in the Kaokoveld, and perhaps the long-nurtured ideal of a national park stretching from the Ugab to the Kunene and eastwards to Namutoni may be realised.

Since 1980 law enforcement by D.N.C. officers, backed up by the auxiliary game guards, has resulted in effective control of the Kaokoveld. Poaching is now at a manageable level and there have been only two rhino and no elephants poached in recent years. Though the situation is relatively stable now the vigilance dare not be relaxed. The insurgency and the state of emergency in the north continues. The demand for ivory is still great and the demand for rhino horn growing.

As the supply of rhino horn from Central and East Africa dwindles, due to the extinction of rhino populations, the price rises. This has pushed the professional rhino horn traders to exploit new sources of supply, such as the rhino populations of the Zambezi valley in Zimbabwe. Rhino are now being taken out at the rate of one animal each day, despite the anti-poaching efforts of the national parks, police and military forces. When these rhino are gone, then the only areas left, easily accessible to poachers operating out of war-ravaged countries where civil order has broken down, will be in Namibia and South Africa. The large rhino population of Etosha will become a prime target, and recent indications are that it is already so. The remaining rhino of the Kaokoveld will also be at risk. In South Africa it can be expected that the Kruger National Park and the Ndumu Game Reserve populations will be the first to be affected.

While elephant numbers in Africa are still high by comparison with rhinos, they are falling rapidly. Within the past five years elephants have virtually been exterminated in the Sudan and Central African Republic and numbers are falling in all countries except in southern Africa. The increase in the price of ivory continues, and the transport system necessary to move ivory still functions efficiently in the southern African countries. Ivory from Zambia and Zaire is being smuggled into South Africa, and shipped from there overseas. The ivory trade has long been active in Namibia, and will no doubt survive, despite the best efforts of the D.N.C.

The Kaokoveld elephants and black rhino must, for the foreseeable future, be regarded as under grave threat. No relaxation of vigilance can be allowed. The formal protection of the areas in which they occur must be promoted at every opportunity. Their acceptance as a permanent and necessary element in the economic, social and political development of the Kaokoland and Damaraland territories must be ensured. Without them the Kaokoveld will become another sterile desert, devoid of its greatest assets. With them it remains as part of the living wilderness of Namibia — one of the greatest wildlife countries in Africa.

68

Checklist of mammals

This list has been compiled from the sources given in the bibliography and is based in particular on the work of Captain G. C. Shortridge, done more than 50 years ago. More recent work, such as that of C. G. Coetzee, P. J. Viljoen and D. M. Avery, as well as our own observations, has been drawn on.

The taxonomic arrangement follows that of R. H. N. Smithers' *Mammals of the Southern African Subregion*, and the numbers used refer to that work. The Cetaceans (whales and dolphins) have not been included. We have not always followed Smithers' use of common names, sometimes preferring those that are well established in the literature. We have also updated a few scientific names.

Soricidae – Shrews
10 Reddish-grey musk shrew   *Crocidura cyanea*
14 Lesser red musk shrew   *Crocidura hirta*

Erinaceidae – Hedgehog
16 South African hedgehog   *Erinaceus frontalis*

Macroscelididae – Elephant-shrews
33 Round-eared elephant shrew   *Macroscelides proboscideus*
36 Smith's rock elephant-shrew   *Elephantulus rupestris*
37 Bushveld elephant-shrew   *Elephantulus intufi*

Pteropodidae – Fruit bats
41 Angolan epauletted fruit bat   *Epomophorus angolensis*
45 Straw-coloured fruit bat   *Eidolon helvum*

Molossidae – Free-tailed bats
52 Flat-headed free-tailed bat   *Sauromys petrophilus*
63 Egyptian free-tailed bat   *Tadarida aegyptiaca*

Vespertilionidae – Vesper bats
67 Schreibers' long-fingered bat   *Miniopterus schreibersii*
69 Angola hairy bat   *Myotis seabrai*
82 Long-tailed serotine bat   *Eptesicus hottentotus*
84 Aloe serotine bat   *Eptesicus zuluensis*
86 Cape serotine bat   *Eptesicus capensis*
88 Yellow house bat   *Scotophilus dinganii*
90 Schlieffen's bat   *Nycticeius schlieffenii*
92 Damara woolly bat   *Kerivoula argentata*

Nycteridae – Slit-faced bats
98 Common slit-faced bat   *Nycteris thebaica*

Rhinolophidae – Horseshoe bats
101 Ruppell's horseshoe bat   *Rhinolophus fumigatus*
102 Geoffroy's horseshoe bat   *Rhinolophus clivosus*
108 Dent's horseshoe bat   *Rhinolophus denti*

Hipposideridae – Leaf-nosed bats
110 Commerson's leaf-nosed bat   *Hipposideros commersoni*
111 Sundevall's leaf-nosed bat   *Hipposideros caffer*

Lorisidae – Bushbabies
115 Lesser bushbaby   *Galago moholi*

Cercopithecidae – Monkeys and baboons
117 Chacma baboon   *Papio ursinus*
119 Vervet monkey   *Cercopithecus aethiops*

Manidae – Pangolin
121 Pangolin   *Manis temminckii*

Leporidae – Hares, rock rabbits
122 Cape hare   *Lepus capensis*
123 Scrub hare   *Lepus saxatilis*
126 Jameson's red rock rabbit   *Pronolagus randensis*

Bathyergidae – Molerats
132 Common molerat   *Cryptomys hottentotus*

Hystricidae – Porcupine
134 Porcupine   *Hystrix africaeaustralis*

Pedetidae – Springhare
135 Springhare   *Pedetes capensis*

Gliridae – Dormice
137 Rock dormouse   *Graphiurus platyops*
138 Woodland dormouse   *Graphiurus murinus*

Sciuridae – Squirrels
140 Ground squirrel   *Xerus inauris*
141 Kaokoveld ground squirrel   *Xerus princeps*
143 Striped tree squirrel   *Funisciurus congicus*
145 Bush squirrel   *Paraxerus cepapi*

Thryonomyidae – Cane-rats
147 Greater cane-rat   *Thryonomys swinderianus*

Petromuridae – Dassie rat
149 Dassie rat   *Petromus typicus*

Cricetidae and Muridae – Rats and mice
151 Littledale's whistling rat   *Parotomys littledalei*
162 Single-striped mouse   *Lemniscomys rosalia*
163 Striped mouse   *Rhabdomys pumilio*
164 Desert pygmy mouse   *Mus indutus*
171 Multimammate mouse   *Mastomys natalensis*
177 Tree rat   *Thallomys paedulcus*
179 Namaqua rock mouse   *Aethomys namaquensis*
181 African bush rat   *Aethomys chrysophilus*
185 Short-tailed gerbil   *Desmodillus auricularis*
186 Hairy-footed gerbil   *Gerbillurus paeba*
189 Setzer's hairy-footed gerbil   *Gerbillurus setzeri*
190 Bushveld gerbil   *Tatera leucogaster*
196 Pouched mouse   *Saccostomus campestris*
197 Large-eared mouse   *Malacothrix typica*
199 Grey climbing mouse   *Dendromus melanotis*
203 Tiny fat mouse   *Steatomys parvus*
206 Pygmy rock mouse   *Petromyscus collinus*

70

Hyaenidae – Aardwolf, hyaenas
244 Aardwolf   *Proteles cristatus*
245 Brown hyaena   *Hyaena brunnea*
246 Spotted hyaena   *Crocuta crocuta*

Felidae – Cats
247 Cheetah   *Acinonyx jubatus*
248 Leopard   *Panthera pardus*
249 Lion   *Panthera leo*
250 Caracal   *Felis caracal*
251 African wild cat   *Felis lybica*

Canidae – Foxes, wild dog, jackal
255 Bat-eared fox   *Otocyon megalotis*
256 Wild dog   *Lycaon pictus*
257 Cape fox   *Vulpes chama*
259 Black-backed jackal   *Canis mesomelas*

Mustelidae – Otter, polecat, honey badger
260 Cape clawless otter   *Aonyx capensis*
261 Spotted-necked otter   *Lutra maculicollis*
262 Honey badger   *Mellivora capensis*
264 Striped polecat   *Ictonyx striatus*

Viverridae – Mongoose, civets, genets, suricate
267 Small-spotted genet   *Genetta genetta*
269 Suricate   *Suricata suricatta*
272 Yellow mongoose   *Cynictis penicillata*
274 Slender mongoose   *Galerella sanguinea*
275 Small grey mongoose   *Galerella pulverulenta*
278 Water mongoose   *Atilax paludinosus*
279 Banded mongoose   *Mungos mungo*
280 Dwarf mongoose   *Helogale parvula*

Otariidae – Fur seal
281 Cape fur seal   *Arctocephalus pusillus*

Orycteropodidae – Antbear
288 Antbear   *Orycteropus afer*

Elephantidae – Elephant
289 African elephant   *Loxodonta africana*

Procaviidae – Hyraxes
290 Rock hyrax   *Procavia capensis*
291 Kaokoveld rock hyrax   *Procavia welwitschii*

Rhinocerotidae – Rhinoceros
296 Black rhinoceros   *Diceros bicornis*

Equidae – Zebras
297 Hartmann's mountain zebra   *Equus zebra hartmannae*
298 Burchell's zebra   *Equus burchelli*

Suidae – Pigs
300 Warthog   *Phacochoerus aethiopicus*

Hippopotamidae – Hippopotamus
302 Hippopotamus   *Hippopotamus amphibius*

Giraffidae – Giraffe
303 Giraffe   *Giraffa camelopardalis*

Bovidae – Antelopes
308 Red hartebeest   *Alcelaphus buselaphus*
313 Grey duiker   *Sylvicapra grimmia*
314 Springbok   *Antidorcas marsupialis*
315 Klipspringer   *Oreotragus oreotragus*
316 Damara dik-dik   *Madoqua kirkii*
318 Steenbok   *Raphicerus campestris*
322 Black-faced impala   *Aepyceros melampus petersi*
327 Gemsbok   *Oryx gazella*
329 Kudu   *Tragelaphus strepsiceros*
333 Eland   *Taurotragus oryx*

72

Checklist of birds

This list has largely been compiled from the published records that appear in the bibliography, together with the recent work of Steven Braine and our own limited observations. The work of Professor J. M. Winterbottom and the reports of C. F. Clinning and R. A. C. Jensen on the birds of Etosha and the Kaokoveld were fundamental in the compilation of this list, and all Etosha records for the Otjovasandu area, as well as Kamanjab records, were incorporated. A further valuable source of information that was freely incorporated was the list of birds of the Skeleton Coast Park published by P. G. Ryan and J. Cooper of the Percy Fitzpatrick Institute of African Ornithology and the late C. J. Stutterheim and Rudi Loutit of the Directorate of Nature Conservation.

A very rough guide to the status of the various species of birds in the Kaokoveld has been given as follows:

B = Definite breeding records
R = Resident species or regular migrant
V = Vagrant or uncommon resident or migrant
S = Sea, inshore or coastal species

The taxonomic arrangement and nomenclature largely follows that of Professor Gordon Maclean in his *Roberts' Birds of Southern Africa* edition of 1984. We have, however, not always followed his usage of common names. In particular, we have retained the hyphens in adjectival bird names, such as 'red-headed finch' rather than 'redheaded finch'. The birds have been arranged in families, and the *Roberts'* number of the 1984 edition given for each species.

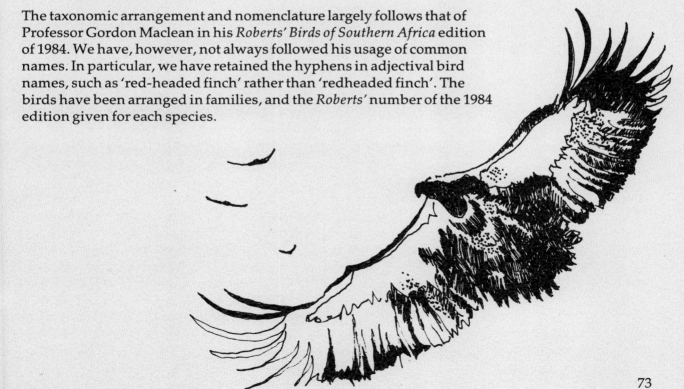

Struthionidae – Ostrich
1 Ostrich	*Struthio camelus*	B

Spheniscidae – Penguins
3 Jackass penguin	*Spheniscus demersus*	V

Podicipedidae – Grebes
7 Black-necked grebe	*Podiceps nigricollis*	R
8 Dabchick	*Tachybaptus ruficollis*	R

Diomedeidae – Albatrosses
10 Wandering albatross	*Diomedea exulans*	S
11 Shy albatross	*Diomedea cauta*	S
12 Black-browed albatross	*Diomedea melanophris*	S
14 Yellow-nosed albatross	*Diomedea chlororhynchos*	S

Procellariidae – Petrels, shearwaters, prions
17 Southern giant petrel	*Macronectes giganteus*	S
18 Northern giant petrel	*Macronectes halli*	S
21 Pintado petrel	*Daption capense*	S
23 Great-winged petrel	*Pterodroma macroptera*	S
24 Soft-plumaged petrel	*Pterodroma mollis*	S
26 Atlantic petrel	*Pterodroma incerta*	S
29 Broad-billed prion	*Pachyptila vittata*	S
32 White-chinned petrel	*Procellaria aequinoctialis*	S
34 Cory's shearwater	*Calonectris diomedea*	S
35 Great shearwater	*Puffinis gravis*	S
37 Sooty shearwater	*Puffinis griseus*	S
38 Manx shearwater	*Puffinis puffinus*	S

Oceanitidae – Storm petrels
42 European storm petrel	*Hydrobates pelagicus*	S
43 Leach's storm petrel	*Oceanodroma leucorhoa*	S
44 Wilson's storm petrel	*Oceanites oceanicus*	S

Pelecanidae – Pelicans
49 White pelican	*Pelecanus onocrotalus*	V

Sulidae – Gannets
53 Cape gannet	*Morus capensis*	R

Phalacrocoracidae – Cormorants
55 White-breasted cormorant	*Phalacrocorax carbo*	B
56 Cape cormorant	*Phalacrocorax capensis*	B
58 Reed cormorant	*Phalacrocorax africanus*	B
59 Crowned cormorant	*Phalacrocorax coronatus*	R
60 Darter	*Anhinga melanogaster*	R

Ardeidae – Herons, egrets
62 Grey heron	*Ardea cinerea*	B
63 Black-headed heron	*Ardea melanocephala*	B
64 Goliath heron	*Ardea goliath*	R
66 Great white egret	*Egretta alba*	R
67 Little egret	*Egretta garzetta*	V
68 Yellow-billed egret	*Egretta intermedia*	V
69 Black egret	*Egretta ardesiaca*	V
71 Cattle egret	*Bubulcus ibis*	V
72 Squacco heron	*Ardeola ralloides*	V
74 Green-backed heron	*Butorides striatus*	R
78 Little bittern	*Ixobrychus minutus*	V

Scopidae – Hamerkop
81 Hamerkop	*Scopus umbretta*	V

Ciconiidae – Storks
83 White stork	*Ciconia ciconia*	V
84 Black stork	*Ciconia nigra*	V
87 Open-billed stork	*Anastomus lamelligerus*	V
90 Yellow-billed stork	*Mycteria ibis*	V

Phoenicopteridae – Flamingoes
96 Greater flamingo	*Phoenicopterus ruber*	R
97 Lesser flamingo	*Phoenicopterus minor*	R

Anatidae – Ducks, geese
99 White-faced duck	*Dendrocygna viduata*	V
101 White-backed duck	*Thalassornis leuconotus*	V
102 Egyptian goose	*Alopochen aegyptiacus*	B
106 Cape teal	*Anas capensis*	B
107 Hottentot teal	*Anas hottentota*	B
108 Red-billed teal	*Anas erythrorhyncha*	B
112 Cape shoveller	*Anas smithii*	R
113 Southern pochard	*Netta erythrophthalma*	V
116 Spurwinged goose	*Plectropterus gambensis*	V
117 Maccoa duck	*Oxyura maccoa*	B

Sagittariidae – Secretary bird
118 Secretary bird	*Sagittarius serpentarius*	V

Accipitridae – Raptors
120 Egyptian vulture	*Neophron percnopterus*	V
123 White-backed vulture	*Gyps africanus*	V
124 Lappet-faced vulture	*Torgos tracheliotus*	B
125 White-headed vulture	*Trigonoceps occipitalis*	V
126 Yellow-billed kite	*Milvus migrans parasitus*	V
126 Black kite	*Milvus migrans migrans*	V
127 Black-shouldered kite	*Elanus caeruleus*	B
131 Black eagle	*Aquila verreauxii*	B
132 Tawny eagle	*Aquila rapax*	B
133 Steppe eagle	*Aquila nipalensis*	V
135 Wahlberg's eagle	*Aquila wahlbergi*	V
136 Booted eagle	*Hieraaetus pennatus*	V
137 African hawk eagle	*Hieraaetus fasciatus*	B
140 Martial eagle	*Polemaetus bellicosus*	B
142 Brown snake eagle	*Circaetus cinereus*	V
143 Black-breasted snake eagle	*Circaetus gallicus*	B
146 Bateleur	*Terathopius ecaudatus*	V
148 African fish eagle	*Haliaeetus vocifer*	R
149 Steppe buzzard	*Buteo buteo*	V
152 Jackal buzzard	*Buteo rufofuscus*	R
153 Augur buzzard	*Buteo augur*	B
157 Little sparrow-hawk	*Accipiter minullus*	B
159 Little banded goshawk	*Accipiter badius*	V
161 Gabar goshawk	*Micronisus gabar*	B
162 Pale chanting goshawk	*Melierax canorus*	B
168 Black harrier	*Circus maurus*	R
169 Gymnogene	*Polyboroides typus*	V

Pandionidae – Osprey
170 Osprey	*Pandion haliaetus*	V

Falconidae – Falcons, kestrels

171 Peregrine	*Falco peregrinus*	B
172 Lanner	*Falco biarmicus*	B
173 Hobby	*Falco subbuteo*	V
178 Red-necked falcon	*Falco chiquera*	B
179 Western red-footed kestrel	*Falco vespertinus*	V
181 Rock kestrel	*Falco tinnunculus*	B
182 Greater kestrel	*Falco rupicoloides*	B
184 Grey kestrel	*Falco ardosiaceus*	V
186 Pygmy falcon	*Polihierax semitorquatus*	V

Phasianidae – Francolins, quails

193 Orange River francolin	*Francolinus levaillantoides*	B
194 Red-billed francolin	*Francolinus adspersus*	B
197 Hartlaub's francolin	*Francolinus hartlaubi*	B
198 Red-necked francolin	*Francolinus afer*	R
199 Swainson's francolin	*Francolinus swainsonii*	V
200 African quail	*Coturnix coturnix*	B
201 Harlequin quail	*Coturnix delegorguei*	V

Numididae – Guinea fowl

203 Helmeted guineafowl	*Numida meleagris*	B

Turnicidae – Button quails

205 Kurrichane button-quail	*Turnix sylvatica*	B

Rallidae – Crakes, gallinule

212 African crake	*Crex egregia*	V
213 Black crake	*Amaurornis flavirostris*	B
214 Spotted crake	*Porzana porzana*	V
223 Purple gallinule	*Porphyrio porphyrio*	R
224 Lesser gallinule	*Porphyrula alleni*	V
226 Moorhen	*Gallinula chloropus*	B
227 Lesser moorhen	*Gallinula angulata*	V
228 Red-knobbed coot	*Fulica cristata*	B

Otididae – Bustards, korhaans

230 Kori bustard	*Ardeotis kori*	R
232 Ludwig's bustard	*Neotis ludwigii*	B
236 Rüppell's korhaan	*Eupodotis rueppellii*	B
237 Red-crested korhaan	*Eupodotis ruficrista*	V
239 Black korhaan	*Eupodotis afra*	R

Jacanidae – Jacana

240 African jacana	*Actophilornis africanus*	V

Rostratulidae – Painted snipe

242 Painted snipe	*Rostratula benghalensis*	V

Haematopodidae – Oystercatcher

244 African black oystercatcher	*Haematopus moquini*	B

Charadriidae – Plovers

245 Ringed plover	*Charadrius hiaticula*	R
246 White-fronted plover	*Charadrius marginatus*	B
247 Chestnut-banded plover	*Charadrius pallidus*	R
248 Kittlitz's plover	*Charadrius pecuarius*	R
249 Three-banded plover	*Charadrius tricollaris*	B
252 Caspian plover	*Charadrius asiaticus*	V
253 Lesser golden plover	*Pluvialis dominica*	V
254 Grey plover	*Pluvialis squatarola*	R
255 Crowned plover	*Vanellus coronatus*	B
258 Blacksmith plover	*Vanellus armatus*	B
262 Turnstone	*Arenaria interpres*	R
263 Terek sandpiper	*Xenus cinereus*	V
264 Common sandpiper	*Tringa hypoleucos*	R
266 Wood sandpiper	*Tringa glareola*	R
269 Marsh sandpiper	*Tringa stagnatilis*	V
270 Greenshank	*Tringa nebularia*	R
271 Knot	*Calidris canutus*	R
272 Curlew sandpiper	*Calidris ferruginea*	R
274 Little stint	*Calidris minuta*	R
277 White-rumped sandpiper	*Calidris fuscicollis*	V
281 Sanderling	*Calidris alba*	R
283 Broad-billed sandpiper	*Limicola falcinellus*	V
284 Ruff, Reeve	*Philomachus pugnax*	R
288 Bar-tailed godwit	*Limosa lapponica*	V
289 Curlew	*Numenius arquata*	V
290 Whimbrel	*Numenius phaeopus*	R
291 Grey phalarope	*Phalaropus fulicarius*	S

Recurvirostridae – Avocets, stilts

294 Avocet	*Recurvirostra avosetta*	B
295 Black-winged stilt	*Himantopus himantopus*	R

Burhinidae – Dikkops

297 Spotted dikkop	*Burhinus capensis*	V
298 Water dikkop	*Burhinus vermiculatus*	V

Glareolidae – Coursers

299 Burchell's courser	*Cursorius rufus*	B
300 Temminck's courser	*Cursorius temminckii*	V
301 Double-banded courser	*Rhinoptilus africanus*	B
303 Bronze-winged courser	*Rhinoptilus chalcopterus*	V

Laridae – Skuas, gulls, terns

307 Arctic skua	*Stercorarius parasiticus*	V
308 Long-tailed skua	*Stercorarius longicaudus*	S
309 Pomarine skua	*Stercorarius pomarinus*	S
310 Subantarctic skua	*Catharacta antarctica*	R
312 Kelp gull	*Larus dominicanus*	B
315 Grey-headed gull	*Larus cirrocephalus*	R
318 Sabine's gull	*Larus sabini*	S
322 Caspian tern	*Hydroprogne caspia*	R
323 Royal tern	*Sterna maxima*	V
324 Swift tern	*Sterna bergii*	V
326 Sandwich tern	*Sterna sandvicensis*	R
327 Common tern	*Sterna hirundo*	R
328 Arctic tern	*Sterna paradisaea*	R
334 Damara tern	*Sterna balaenarum*	B
337 Black tern	*Chlidonias niger*	R
339 White-winged black tern	*Chlidonias leucopterus*	V

Pteroclidae – Sandgrouse

344 Namaqua sandgrouse	*Pterocles namaqua*	B
345 Burchell's sandgrouse	*Pterocles burchelli*	V
347 Double-banded sandgrouse	*Pterocles bicinctus*	B

Columbidae – Pigeons, doves

349 Rock pigeon	*Columba guinea*	B
352 Red-eyed dove	*Streptopelia semitorquata*	V
353 Mourning dove	*Streptopelia decipiens*	R
354 Cape turtle dove	*Streptopelia capicola*	R
355 Laughing dove	*Streptopelia senegalensis*	R
356 Namaqua dove	*Oena capensis*	B
358 Emerald-spotted wood dove	*Turtur chalcospilos*	R
361 Green pigeon	*Treron calva*	V

Psittacidae – Parrots

365 Rüppell's parrot	*Poicephalus rueppellii*	R
367 Rosy-faced lovebird	*Agapornis roseicollis*	R

Musophagidae – Touracos

373 Grey loerie	*Corythaixoides concolor*	B

Cuculidae – Cuckoos, coucals

375 African cuckoo	*Cuculus gularis*	V
378 Black cuckoo	*Cuculus clamosus*	V
380 Great spotted cuckoo	*Clamator glandarius*	V
382 Jacobin cuckoo	*Clamator jacobinus*	V
385 Klaas's cuckoo	*Chrysococcyx klaas*	V
386 Diederik cuckoo	*Chrysococcyx caprius*	B
390 Senegal coucal	*Centropus senegalensis*	V

Tytonidae – Barn and grass owls

392 Barn owl	*Tyto alba*	B

Strigidae – Typical owls

395 Marsh owl	*Asio capensis*	B
396 Scops owl	*Otus senegalensis*	R
397 White-faced owl	*Otus leucotis*	R
398 Pearl-spotted owl	*Glaucidium perlatum*	B
401 Spotted eagle owl	*Bubo africanus*	B
402 Giant eagle owl	*Bubo lacteus*	B

Caprimulgidae – Nightjars

406 Rufous-cheeked nightjar	*Caprimulgus rufigena*	B
408 Freckled nightjar	*Caprimulgus tristigma*	R
409 Mozambique nightjar	*Caprimulgus fossii*	R

Apodidae – Swifts

411 European swift	*Apus apus*	V
413 Bradfield's swift	*Apus bradfieldi*	B
415 White-rumped swift	*Apus caffer*	V
417 Little swift	*Apus affinis*	B
418 Alpine swift	*Apus melba*	V
421 Palm swift	*Cypsiurus parvus*	B

Colliidae – Mousebirds

425 White-backed mousebird	*Colius colius*	B
426 Red-faced mousebird	*Colius indicus*	B

Alcedinidae – Kingfishers

428 Pied kingfisher	*Ceryle rudis*	R
429 Giant kingfisher	*Ceryle maxima*	V
431 Malachite kingfisher	*Alcedo cristata*	V
433 Woodland kingfisher	*Halcyon senegalensis*	V
436 Grey-hooded kingfisher	*Halcyon leucocephala*	R

Meropidae – Bee-eaters

438 European bee-eater	*Merops apiaster*	V
439 Olive bee-eater	*Merops superciliosus*	B
444 Little bee-eater	*Merops pusillus*	V
445 Swallow-tailed bee-eater	*Merops hirundineus*	R

Coraciidae – Rollers

447 Lilac-breasted roller	*Coracias caudata*	R
449 Purple roller	*Coracias naevia*	V

Upupidae – Hoopoe

451 Hoopoe	*Upupa epops*	R

Phoeniculidae – Woodhoopoes

452 Red-billed woodhoopoe	*Phoeniculus purpureus*	R
453 Violet woodhoopoe	*Phoeniculus damarensis*	R
454 Scimitarbill	*Phoeniculus cyanomelas*	B

Bucerotidae – Hornbills

457 Grey hornbill	*Tockus nasutus*	V
458 Red-billed hornbill	*Tockus erythrorhynchus*	R
459 Yellow-billed hornbill	*Tockus flavirostris*	B
462 Monteiro's hornbill	*Tockus monteiri*	R

Capitonidae – Barbets

465 Pied barbet	*Lybius leucomelas*	V
470 Yellow-fronted tinker barbet	*Pogoniulus chrysoconus*	V

Indicatoridae – Honeyguides

474 Greater honeyguide	*Indicator indicator*	V
476 Lesser honeyguide	*Indicator minor*	V

Picidae – Woodpeckers

481 Bennett's woodpecker	*Campethera bennettii*	R
483 Golden-tailed woodpecker	*Campethera abingoni*	R
486 Cardinal woodpecker	*Dendropicos fuscescens*	R
487 Bearded woodpecker	*Thripias namaquus*	R

Alaudidae – Larks
493 Monotonous lark	*Mirafra passerina*	V
494 Rufous-naped lark	*Mirafra africana*	V
495 Clapper lark	*Mirafra apiata*	V
497 Fawn-coloured lark	*Mirafra africanoides*	V
498 Sabota lark	*Mirafra sabota*	R
500 Long-billed lark	*Mirafra curvirostris*	R
505 Dusky lark	*Pinarocorys nigricans*	V
506 Spike-heeled lark	*Chersomanes albofasciata*	R
507 Red-capped lark	*Calandrella cinerea*	R
511 Stark's lark	*Alauda starki*	R
514 Gray's lark	*Ammomanes grayi*	R
515 Chestnut-backed finch-lark	*Eremopterix leucotis*	R
516 Grey-backed finch-lark	*Eremopterix verticalis*	B

Hirundinidae – Swallows, martins
518 European swallow	*Hirundo rustica*	R
520 White-throated swallow	*Hirundo albigularis*	V
522 Wire-tailed swallow	*Hirundo smithii*	R
523 Pearl-breasted swallow	*Hirundo dimidiata*	V
526 Greater striped swallow	*Hirundo cucullata*	V
527 Lesser striped swallow	*Hirundo abyssinica*	V
529 Rock martin	*Hirundo fuligula*	B
530 House martin	*Delichon urbica*	V
532 Sand martin	*Riparia riparia*	V
533 Brown-throated martin	*Riparia paludicola*	R

Campephagidae – Cuckoo shrikes
538 Black cuckoo shrike	*Campephaga flava*	V
539 White-breasted cuckoo shrike	*Coracina pectoralis*	V

Dicruridae – Drongos
541 Fork-tailed drongo	*Dicrurus adsimilis*	R

Oriolidae – Orioles
543 European golden oriole	*Oriolus oriolus*	V
544 African golden oriole	*Oriolus auratus*	V
545 Black-headed oriole	*Oriolus larvatus*	V

Corvidae – Crows
547 Black crow	*Corvus capensis*	B
548 Pied crow	*Corvus albus*	B

Paridae – Tits
552 Ashy tit	*Parus cinerascens*	V
555 Carp's black tit	*Parus carpi*	B
557 Cape penduline tit	*Anthoscopus minutus*	V

Timaliidae – Babblers
561 Black-faced babbler	*Turdoides melanops*	V
563 Pied babbler	*Turdoides bicolor*	V
564 Bare-cheecked babbler	*Turdoides gymnogenys*	B

Pycnonotidae – Bulbuls
567 Red-eyed bulbul	*Pycnonotus nigricans*	B
574 Yellow-bellied bulbul	*Chlorocichla flaviventris*	R

Turdidae – Thrushes, chats, robins
580 Groundscraper thrush	*Turdus litsitsirupa*	R
583 Short-toed rock thrush	*Monticola brevipes*	R
586 Mountain chat	*Oenanthe monticola*	B
587 Capped wheatear	*Oenanthe pileata*	V
589 Familiar chat	*Cercomela familiaris*	B
590 Tractrac chat	*Cercomela tractrac*	B
592 Karoo chat	*Cercomela schlegelii*	V
595 Ant-eating chat	*Myrmecocichla formicivora*	V
604 Rufous-tailed palm thrush	*Cichladusa ruficauda*	V
613 White-browed robin	*Erythropygia leucophrys*	R
615 Kalahari robin	*Erythropygia paena*	R
618 Herero chat	*Namibornis herero*	B

Sylviidae – Warblers, cisticolas, prinias
621 Tit babbler	*Parisoma subcaeruleum*	B
631 African marsh warbler	*Acrocephalus baeticatus*	B
634 European sedge warbler	*Acrocephalus schoenobaenus*	R
635 Lesser swamp warbler	*Acrocephalus gracilirostris*	V
643 Willow warbler	*Phylloscopus trochilus*	R
648 Yellow-breasted apalis	*Apalis flavida*	V
651 Long-billed crombec	*Sylvietta rufescens*	B
653 Yellow-bellied eremomela	*Eremomela icteropygialis*	B
656 Burnt-necked eremomela	*Eremomela usticollis*	V
657 Bleating warbler	*Camaroptera brachyura*	B
658 Barred warbler	*Camaroptera fasciolata*	V
662 Damara rock-jumper	*Achaetops pycnopygius*	B
664 Fan-tailed cisticola	*Cisticola juncidis*	B
665 Desert cisticola	*Cisticola aridula*	V
669 Grey-backed cisticola	*Cisticola subruficapilla*	B
671 Tinkling cisticola	*Cisticola rufilata*	B
672 Rattling cisticola	*Cisticola chiniana*	R
683 Tawny-flanked prinia	*Prinia subflava*	R
685 Black-chested prinia	*Prinia flavicans*	B

Muscicapidae – Flycatchers
689 Spotted flycatcher	*Muscicapa striata*	R
691 Blue-grey flycatcher	*Muscicapa caerulescens*	V
695 Marico flycatcher	*Melaenornis mariquensis*	B
697 Chat flycatcher	*Melaenornis infuscatus*	V
703 Pririt batis	*Batis pririt*	V
710 Paradise flycatcher	*Terpsiphone viridis*	R

Motacillidae – Wagtails

711 African pied wagtail	*Motacilla aguimp*	R
713 Cape wagtail	*Motacilla capensis*	B
714 Yellow wagtail	*Motacilla flava*	V
716 Richard's pipit	*Anthus novaeseelandiae*	R
717 Long-billed pipit	*Anthus similis*	R
719 Buffy pipit	*Anthus vaalensis*	V
722 Tree pipit	*Anthus trivialis*	V

Laniidae – Shrikes

731 Lesser grey shrike	*Lanius minor*	V
732 Fiscal shrike	*Lanius collaris*	B
735 Long-tailed shrike	*Corvinella melanoleuca*	V
738 Swamp boubou	*Laniarius bicolor*	R
739 Crimson-breasted shrike	*Laniarius atrococcineus*	R
740 Puffback shrike	*Dryoscopus cubla*	R
741 Brubru	*Nilaus afer*	R
743 Three-streaked tchagra	*Tchagra australis*	R
744 Black-crowned tchagra	*Tchagra senegala*	V
746 Bokmakierie	*Telophorus zeylonus*	B
748 Orange-breasted bush shrike	*Telophorus sulfureopectus*	V
751 Grey-headed bush shrike	*Malaconotus blanchoti*	V
752 White-tailed shrike	*Lanioturdus torquatus*	B

Prionopidae – Helmetshrikes

753 White helmetshrike	*Prionops plumatus*	V
754 Red-billed helmetshrike	*Prionops retzii*	V
756 White-crowned shrike	*Eurocephalus anguitimens*	R

Sturnidae – Starlings

760 Wattled starling	*Creatophora cinerea*	V
761 Plum-coloured starling	*Cinnyricinclus leucogaster*	R
763 Long-tailed starling	*Lamprotornis mevesii*	R
764 Cape glossy starling	*Lamprotornis nitens*	R
770 Pale-winged starling	*Onychognathus nabouroup*	B

Buphagidae – Oxpeckers

771 Yellow-billed oxpecker	*Buphagus africanus*	V
772 Red-billed oxpecker	*Buphagus erythrorhynchus*	V

Nectariniidae – Sunbirds

787 White-bellied sunbird	*Nectarinia talatala*	V
788 Dusky sunbird	*Nectarinia fusca*	B
791 Scarlet-chested sunbird	*Nectarinia senegalensis*	V

Ploceidae – Weavers, sparrows

798 Red-billed buffalo weaver	*Bubalornis niger*	B
799 White-browed sparrow-weaver	*Plocepasser mahali*	R
800 Sociable weaver	*Philetairus socius*	R
801 House sparrow	*Passer domesticus*	B
802 Great sparrow	*Passer motitensis*	B
803 Cape sparrow	*Passer melanurus*	B
804 Grey-headed sparrow	*Passer griseus*	B
806 Scaly-feathered finch	*Sporopipes squamifrons*	B
810 Spectacled weaver	*Ploceus ocularis*	B
812 Chestnut weaver	*Ploceus rubiginosus*	B
814 Masked weaver	*Ploceus velatus*	B
815 Lesser masked weaver	*Ploceus intermedius*	B
816 Golden weaver	*Ploceus xanthops*	B
821 Red-billed quelea	*Quelea quelea*	R
826 Golden bishop	*Euplectes afer*	V

Estrildidae – Waxbills, finches

834 Melba finch	*Pytilia melba*	R
841 Jameson's firefinch	*Lagonosticta rhodopareia*	R
842 Red-billed firefinch	*Lagonosticta senegala*	R
844 Blue waxbill	*Uraeginthus angolensis*	R
845 Violet-eared waxbill	*Uraeginthus granatinus*	V
846 Common waxbill	*Estrilda astrild*	R
847 Black-cheeked waxbill	*Estrilda erythronotos*	R
849 Cinderella waxbill	*Estrilda thomensis*	B
852 Quail finch	*Ortygospiza atricollis*	V
856 Red-headed finch	*Amadina erythrocephala*	B
861 Shaft-tailed whydah	*Vidua regia*	V
862 Paradise whydah	*Vidua paradisea*	V
867 Steel-blue widowfinch	*Vidua chalybeata*	V

Fringillidae – Canaries, buntings

870 Black-throated canary	*Serinus atrogularis*	R
878 Yellow canary	*Serinus flaviventris*	V
879 White-throated canary	*Serinus albogularis*	B
884 Golden-breasted bunting	*Emberiza flaviventris*	V
885 Cape bunting	*Emberiza capensis*	R
886 Rock bunting	*Emberiza tahapisi*	V
887 Lark-like bunting	*Emberiza impetuani*	B

Preceding page Elephants and giraffes on a petroglyph – evidence that these animals have long been living in the Kaokoveld.

Left Rock outcrops dwarfed by vast plains in the western Kaokoveld.

Above Criss-crossing game tracks on a dune slope, cracked layers of ancient mud along the normally dry riverbeds and strange, bare circular patches reflect some of the textures of the Kaokoveld.

81

Elephants, ancient dwellers in the Kaokoveld,
question an intrusion by modern man.

Such pitiful remains could be man's only inheritance in the Kaokoveld if the current renewed interest in the conservation of the area flags or fails.

Overleaf Vast solitude is the essential feature of the Kaokoveld landscape.

The infinite variety of rocks and sand colours the stark landscape.

89

Mountain ramparts have shielded the soft sandy
core of the inner Namib Desert from intruders for
many centuries (also overleaf).

Where the elements have conquered the mountains, the resultant plains are covered in grass during years of abundant rain.

Below Marienfluss.

Bottom Huab Valley.

Left A solitary tree highlights the vastness of a grassy plain.

The inhospitable Skeleton Coast guards the
western approaches to the Kaokoveld.

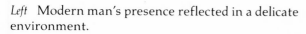

Left   Modern man's presence reflected in a delicate environment.

Above   The restless sea pounds a desolate shore; a washed up seal skull and foraging gulls are indicators of the teeming life off the Skeleton Coast.

Right   Time-smoothed pebbles line the tide-mark along the Skeleton Coast.

Left Water, key to survival in the desert.

Above Storm clouds over the desert offer the promise of renewed life; fog shrouds a lone wind-sculpted tree on the desert dune fringe at Gonias; rain in the mountains, respite to all desert dwellers.

101

Above Life-sustaining water.

Facing page Wet rocks glisten as though gilded
after a brief shower of desert rain.

Facing page River courses – lifelines into the desert from the eastern escarpment.

Top Sunlight and water, dual vital links in the energy cycle of the desert.

Right: above Floods are infrequent and brief but all-important to sustain life of many forms.

Right: below A lush oasis in harsh surroundings.

Tenacious desert-adapted trees grow where no rooting seems possible.

Left Tender blades of grass trace idle patterns in the desert sand.

Above Sun-dappled grasslands burst forth after rains, offering sustenance to a variety of herbivores.

Welwitschias – ancient plants which today harbour and nourish many more recent forms of life.

Facing page Tsamma melons – storehouses of water for wildlife and the informed traveller.

Overleaf Springbok bound in exuberant display across their seemingly inhospitable desert landscape.

Damara dik-dik *(left)* and steenbok *(right)*.

Facing page Black-faced impala, rare resident of the Kaokoveld.

Below Thoughtlessly-placed fences impose a horrible death sentence on many forms of desert wildlife.

Above Hartmann's Valley, home of the hardy gemsbok; spotted hyaenas roam the plains to harvest those who die there; ostriches line up as if for inspection on the plains near Purros.

Left Primarily denizens of the bushveld, giraffes have nevertheless adapted to life in the desert.

117

Hartmann's mountain zebras scatter towards the
fog-shrouded fringes of Hartmann's Valley.

Right Masters of ambush await the unwary intruder.

Pied crow *(left)* and Kori bustard *(right)* – winged
scavengers of the Kaokoveld.

Overleaf Elephants must move many miles
between food and water sources.

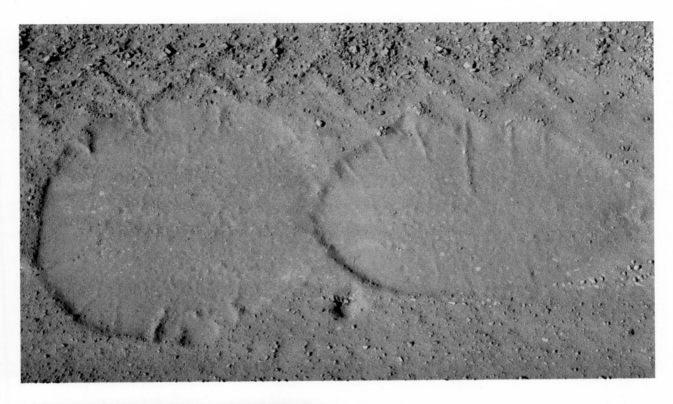

Facing page Characteristic tusk curve of the desert-dwelling elephants.

Above Huge foot-prints are silent testimony that the giants have passed this way.

Left Their feet are adapted for moving across desert dunes and rocky mountains with surprising ease and agility.

Below The harsh environment takes its toll in broken tusks.

Above: left The ancient elephant path leads to an isolated waterhole.

Above: right Even apparently dead twigs may mean the difference between life and death.

Left At home even in the dune belt along the coast, the elephants utilise all the available resources.

Facing page Dwarfed by the vastness of the landscape, a herd of elephants moves slowly into view.

Left Dust cloud marks the agitation of uneasy elephants.

Above Elephant in musth – approach with care.

Below A mud-bath offers relief from the searing heat, and provides a protective mudpack.

Left Polished rubbing stone reveals to the trained eye the presence of black rhinoceroses.

Above No more than a speck, a black rhino against the majestic backdrop of the escarpment foothills.

131

Facing page Lethal behemoth challenging the unwary intruder.

Above Supreme confidence guarding its home ground.

Left Black rhinoceros track in mud – often the only evidence Kaokoveld travellers find of this elusive herbivore.

Below Totally at home in the desert, black rhino feed on whatever may be available.

Facing page Armoured yet vulnerable, black rhino sometimes succumb to natural environmental stresses.

Above Grimace of death, but the presence of the horn shows that this rhinoceros died of natural causes rather than the poacher's bullet.

Right Timely action by the Directorate of Nature Conservation has established a reserve nucleus of Kaokoveld black rhino in Etosha.

Facing page   Signposts of the past: petroglyphs testify to the presence of ancient man in this desert environment.

Above   Colourful garb of Herero women contrasts joyfully with the subdued tones of their countryside.

Right   Modern modes of travel have been adopted where stout legs once sufficed.

Facing page Face of an old man reflects the wisdom of the survivor.

Above: left Sunbaked kraal protects an isolated Ovahimba dwelling.

Above: right The view from within.

Right Natural material is used to construct a holding pen for local poultry.

Right: below Skulls of slaughtered cattle line the grave of a local headman – those on one side to speed him on his journey into the unknown, those on the other to serve as solace to all left behind.

Above Survival of the group depends on sturdy children.

Left Whimsical, innocent, a youngster faces the future with slight bemusement.

Facing page Dignified and serene, she displays her characteristic Ovahimba jewellery.

Overleaf Proud and steeped in ancient culture, this woman is evidently of high local stature.

Bibliography

We give below a list of the most important publications consulted in the preparation of this text. This list is by no means exhaustive. For ease of reference the bibliography has been arranged under subject headings.

Natural History and Conservation

Lambrechts, H. A. 1985. *Namibia — A Thirstland Wilderness*. Cape Town, Struik.

Owen-Smith, G. L. 1971. The Kaokoveld: An Ecological Base for Future Development Planning. Pinetown, typescript, 67 pp.

—— 1972. Proposals for a game reserve in the Western Kaokoveld. *S. Afr. J. Sci.* 68 (2): 29-37.

Schoeman, Amy. 1984. *Skeleton Coast*. Johannesburg, Macmillan.

Birds

Clancey, P. A. 1985. *The Rare Birds of Southern Africa.* Johannesburg, Winchester Press.

Clinning, C. F. 1978. The biology and conservation of the Damara tern in South West Africa. *Madoqua* 11(1): 31-39.

Clinning C. F. and W. R. Tarboton. 1972. Notes on the Damara rockjumper, *Achaetops pycnopygius. Madoqua* Ser. 1, No. 5: 57-62.

Clinning, C. F. and R. A. C. Jensen. 1977. Additions to the bird checklist of Etosha National Park. *Madoqua* 10(2): 143-148.

——1979. Additions to the bird check-list of Kaokoland and the Skeleton Coast. *Madoqua* 11 (3): 247-253.

Dixon, J. E. W. 1970. Miscellaneous notes on South West African birds. *Madoqua* 2: 45-47.

Frost, P. G. H. and G. Shaughnessy. 1976. Breeding adaptations of the Damara tern *Sterna balaenarum. Madoqua* 9(3): 33-40.

Macdonald, J. D. and B. P. Hall. 1957. Ornithological results of the Bernard Carp/Transvaal Museum expedition to the Kaokoveld, 1951. *Ann. Tvl. Mus.* 23: 1-39.

Maclean, G. L. 1974. Arid-zone adaptations in Southern African birds. *Cimbebasia* Ser. A 2(15): 163-176.

—— 1985. *Roberts' Birds of Southern Africa.* John Voelcker Bird Book Fund, Cape Town.

Ryan, P. G., J. Cooper, C. J. Stutterheim and R. Loutit. 1984. An annotated list of the birds of the Skeleton Coast Park. *Madoqua* 14 (1): 79-90.

Willoughby, E. J. 1971. Biology of larks (Aves: Alaudidae) in the central Namib desert. *Zoologica africana* 6 (1): 133-176.

Winterbottom, J. M. 1964. Results of the Percy Fitzpatrick Institute-Windhoek State Museum Joint Ornithological Expeditions: Report on the Birds of Game Reserve No. 2. *Cimbebasia* 9: 1-75.

—— 1966. Results of the Percy Fitzpatrick Institute-Windhoek State Museum Joint Ornithological Expeditions: 5. Report on the Birds of the Kaokoveld and Kunene River. *Cimbebasia* 19: 1-71.

—— 1967. On some birds of the Kunene River, South West Africa. *Ostrich* 38(2): 155.

Mammals

Avery, D. M. 1986. Micromammals from owl pellets in the Skeleton Coast Park, SWA/Namibia. *Madoqua* 14(4): 389-396.

Joubert, E. 1971. The past and present distribution and status of the black rhinoceros *(Diceros bicornis* Linn. 1758) in South West Africa. *Madoqua* Ser. 1, No. 4: 33-44.

Joubert E. and F. C. Eloff. 1971. Notes on the ecology and behaviour of the black rhinoceros *Diceros bicornis* Linn. 1758 in South West Africa. *Madoqua* Ser. 1, No. 3: 5-54.

Joubert, E. and P. M. K. Mostert. 1975. Distribution patterns and status of some mammals in South West Africa. *Madoqua* 9(1): 5-44.

Loutit, B. D., G. N. Louw and M. K. Seely. 1987. First approximation of food preferences and the chemical composition of the diet of the desert-dwelling black rhinoceros, *Diceros bicornis* L. *Madoqua* 15(1): 35-54.

Shortridge, G. C. 1934. *The Mammals of South West Africa*. London, Heinemann.

Smithers, R. H. N. 1983. *The Mammals of the Southern African Subregion*. Pretoria, University of Pretoria.

Stuart, C. T. 1975. Preliminary notes on the mammals of the Namib Desert Park. *Madoqua* Ser. II (4): 5-68.

Tinley, K. L. 1969. Dikdik *Madoqua kirkii* in South West Africa: Notes on distribution, ecology and behaviour. *Madoqua* 1: 7-34.

Viljoen, P. J. 1982. The distribution and population status of the larger mammals in Kaokoland, South West Africa/Namibia. *Cimbebasia* Ser. A 7(5): 5-33.

—— 1987. Status and past and present distribution of elephants in the Kaokoveld, South West Africa/Namibia. *S. Afr. J. Zool.* 22(4): 247-257.

Withers, P. C. 1979. Ecology of a small mammal community on a rocky outcrop in the Namib Desert. *Madoqua* 11(3): 229-246.

Botany

Giess, W. 1968. A short report on the vegetation of the Namib coastal area from Swakopmund to Cape Frio. *Dinteria* 1: 13-29.

—— 1971. Eine vorlaufige Vegetationskarte von Sudwestafrica. *Dinteria* 4: 1-114.

Malan, J. S. and G. L. Owen-Smith. 1974. The ethnobotany of Kaokoland. *Cimbebasia* Ser. B 2(5): 131-178.

Viljoen P. J. 1980. Veldtipes, verspreiding van die groter soogdiere, en enkele aspekte van die ekologie van Kaokoland. Univ. of Pretoria, M.Sc. thesis.

Archaeology

Hitzeroth, H. W. 1976. On the identity of the stone-working Tjimba, South West Africa. A comparative study based on fingerprint pattern frequencies. *Cimbebasia* Ser. B 2(7): 187-202.

—— 1976. On the identity of the stone-working Tjimba of South West Africa. A comparative multivariate anthropometric analysis. *Cimbebasia* Ser. B 2(9): 209-226.

Kinahan, J. and J. H. A. Kinahan. Holocene subsistence and settlement on the Namib Coast: the example of the Ugab River Mouth. *Cimbebasia* (B) 4(6): 59-72.

Maccalman, H. R. and B. J. Grobbelaar. 1965. Preliminary report of two stone-working OvaTjimba groups in the northern Kaokoveld of South West Africa. *Cimbebasia* 13: 1-39.

Malan, J. S. 1973. Double descent among the Himba of South West Africa. *Cimbebasia* Ser. B. 2(3): 81-112.

—— 1974. The Herero-speaking peoples of Kaokoland. *Cimbebasia* Ser. B 2(4): 113-129.

Van Warmelo, N. J. 1962. *Notes on the Kaokoveld (South West Africa) and its people. Ethnological Publications 26.* Pretoria, Government Printer.

Viereck, A. and J. Rudner. 1957. Twyfelfontein — a centre of prehistoric art in South West Africa. *S. Afr. Arch. Bull.* 12: 15-26.

Wadley, L. 1979. Big Elephant Shelter and its role in the holocene prehistory of central South West Africa. *Cimbebasia* Ser. B. 3(1): 1-76.